# Alice's London Adventures
# in Wonderland

About the Author

From an early age, artist and writer Sarah Elizabeth Beaumont has been fascinated by 'Alice in Wonderland'. From receiving her first pop-up book as a child, her passion for Lewis Carroll's beloved work has led her to travel the globe, gathering editions in many different languages and illustrated in very different styles. There is no doubt that 'Alice in Wonderland' has been a life-long obsession.

In her newest venture, Beaumont combines her talents to create an all-new illustrated parody on Lewis Carroll's classic, which fits surprisingly comfortably into modern London. Beaumont's knowledge of London, together with her affection for Lewis Carroll's timeless fantasy, results in a thoroughly enjoyable romp through England's capital city, whilst poking fun at modern life.

# Alice's London Adventures in Wonderland

*Lewis Carroll and Sarah Elizabeth Beaumont*

*Illustrated by Sarah Elizabeth Beaumont*
*after Sir John Tenniel*

Two Monkeys Publishing

© 2015 Sarah Elizabeth Beaumont
First printing 2015
ISBN 978-0-9932055-0-7
Published by Two Monkeys Publishing
39 Hampstead House, 176 Finchley Road,
London NW3 6BT

Alice's Adventures in Wonderland by Lewis Carroll was originally published in book form in 1865.

Printed in England

*Dedicated to the memory of my dad who loved London*

# Contents

Down the Tunnel at Knightsbridge................................................1

The Pool of Tears in Trafalgar Square.........................................14

A Caucus Race and a Long Tale in Parliament Square...............21

The Rabbit Sends in a Little Bill at Buckingham Palace............28

Advice from a Caterpillar on the Edgware Road.......................38

Pig and Pepper in Camden Town.................................................44

A Mad Take-away in Regents Park................................................52

The Queen's Croquet Ground at London Zoo..........................60

The Mock Turtle's Story at Mornington Crescent.....................67

The Parking Quadrille....................................................................73

The Trial Begins.............................................................................81

Alice's Evidence............................................................................86

## Chapter I

# Down the Tunnel at Knightsbridge

Alice was beginning to get very tired of sitting by her sister on the banks of the Serpentine, and of having nothing to do: once or twice she had peeped into the book her sister was reading, but it had no pictures or conversations in it, "and what is the use of a book," thought Alice, "without pictures or conversations?"

She watched the holiday-makers, who were boating on the lake, and occasionally her gaze drifted to the London Eye, which was visible above the tree-line, rotating almost imperceptibly.

So she was considering in her own mind (as well as she could, for the hot London day made her feel very sleepy and stupid) whether the pleasure of making a daisy-chain would be worth the trouble of getting up and picking the daisies, when suddenly a White Rabbit with pink eyes ran close by her.

There was nothing so very remarkable in that: nor did Alice think it so very much out of the way to hear the rabbit say to itself, "Oh dear, oh dear! I shall be too late" (when she thought it over afterwards, it occurred to her that she ought to have wondered at this, but at the time it all seemed quite natural); but when the Rabbit actually *took a watch out of its waistcoat-pocket,* and looked at it, and then hurried on, Alice started to her feet, for it flashed across her mind that she had never before seen a rabbit with either a waistcoat-pocket, or a watch to take out of it, and burning with curiosity, she got to her feet and began to follow it.

In its hurry, the Rabbit dropped a piece of paper it had been holding and Alice paused for a moment to pick it up, before dodging an in-line skater and continuing her pursuit.

The Rabbit was moving at quite a pace and Alice soon found herself walking briskly along Knightsbridge to keep up with it, past the Hyde Park Barracks and its 33-storey tower, and amongst the smart boutiques and designer shops with their fashionable window displays, towards Harrods.

She was nearly out of breath when she caught sight of the Rabbit disappearing into the entrance of a tube station. She was hard on its heels as it ran through the barriers, and onto a descending escalator.

In another moment, down went Alice after it, never once

considering where it was going, or how in the world she was to get out again.

The escalator dipped suddenly down, so suddenly that Alice had not a moment to think about stopping herself descending what seemed to be a very long staircase.

Either the station was very deep underground, or the escalator moved very slowly, for she had plenty of time as she went down to look about her and wonder what was going to happen next.

First, she tried to look down and make out what she was coming to, but it was too difficult to see anything with the number of people that stood ahead of her; then she looked at the sides of the escalator, and noticed that they were filled with pictures and advertisements, depicting lots of events and attractions.

There were adverts for shows, books and telephone networks, and for websites where one could buy last-minute tickets. There were also advertisements for teeth-whitening, self tanning, hair extensions, and laser eye-surgery. In fact, thought Alice, if she followed all these suggestions, by the time she reached the bottom – where-ever that was – she could have transformed herself into an entirely different person altogether.

Down, down, down. Would the fall never come to an end? "I wonder how many miles I've fallen by this time?" she said aloud. "I must be getting somewhere near the centre of the earth. Let me see: that would be four thousand miles down, I think, and escalators travel at a rate of between one and two feet per second, with a typical angle of inclination to the horizontal floor level of about 30 degrees –" (for, you see, Alice had learnt several things of this sort in her lessons in the schoolroom, and though this was not a very good opportunity for showing off her knowledge, as no one seemed to be listening to her, still it was good practice to say it over) "– why, that would take forever! I wonder what Latitude or Longitude I've got to?" (Alice had no idea what Latitude was, or Longitude either, but thought they were nice grand words to say.)

Presently she began again. "I wonder if I shall fall right through the earth! How funny it'll seem to come out among the people that walk with their heads downward! The Antipathies, I think -" (she was rather glad there was no one listening, this time, as it didn't sound at all the right word) "- but I shall have to ask them what the name of the country is, you know. Please, Ma'am, is this New Zealand or Australia?" (and she tried to curtsey as she spoke) "What an ignorant little girl she'll think me for asking! I wonder if Sydney or Melbourne has a subway system? Perhaps I could find out where I've got to without asking - if the platform had a name on it!"

Down, down, down. There was nothing else to do, so Alice soon began talking again. "I know that New York City has a subway system; it has the most stations and the longest amount of track. And I've read that Seoul Metropolitan Subway is the world's most extensive subway, and the second most highly used, only to Tokyo... Interestingly -" (Alice was now in her element reciting facts she remembered from the schoolroom, knowing that there was no one around to check if they were accurate) "- London's is the oldest subway system in the world, and it's first tunnels were built just below the surface, whereas later lines were laid through circular tunnels dug at a deeper level into the London clay. That is why it is referred to as 'the Tube'."

As the descent continued, Alice began to muse more about her current situation.

"Dinah'll miss me very much tonight, I should think!" (Dinah was the cat.) "I hope they'll remember her saucer of milk at tea-time. Dinah my dear! I wish you were down here with me!"

Suddenly, she was at the bottom, and the descent was over.

Alice was not a bit hurt, and she jumped from the bottom of the moving staircase a moment before the metal step on which she had been standing disappeared into the floor. Before her was a long passage, and the White Rabbit was still in sight, hurrying down it. There was not a moment to be lost: away went Alice like the wind, and was just in time to hear it say, as it turned a corner, "Oh my ears and whiskers, how late it's getting!"

She was close behind it when she turned the corner, but the Rabbit was no longer to be seen: she found herself on a long, empty tube station platform, which was lit by a row of dim lamps hanging from the roof.

It was not the brightly lit busy station she was expecting to see, but instead it was deserted and eerie as if it had been disused for sometime.

There were dusty dog-eared posters all along the platform advertising such things as the London Evening News and the Beatles exhibit newly opening at Madame Tussauds.

When Alice had been all the way down the platform, wondering where the Rabbit had disappeared to, she walked sadly back, wondering how she was ever to get out again.

Alice realised, as she stood frightened and all alone, that she was still holding the piece of paper that the Rabbit had dropped, so she looked at it. It seemed to be a party invitation, for it read: *"You are invited to a Masked Ball today. Your admittance is guaranteed with this invitation. RSVP."*

This sounded very exciting to Alice. She had neither attended a Masked Ball before, nor had even been invited to one. The only difficulty was that there was no address on it, and Alice did not have the slightest idea where the party was to be held, let alone how she could reply to the invitation.

Suddenly, she heard a low drone from far off but getting nearer, and her face was very soon struck by a strong wind coming from the black mouth of the underground tunnel. A dim light came into sight from the darkness within, and then, with an explosive thundering roar, a tube train emerged and clattered past her into the station, slowing down with a raucous screech of brakes.

She could see through the windows that the train was empty. As it came to a violent halt, the doors slid open and the train stood as if it was waiting for her to get on.

Through the window of the nearest carriage, Alice caught sight of a poster that was just like the invitation she was holding, advertising the Masked Ball. How she longed to find the Rabbit again and go to the party.

Without further thought, she jumped onto the train, and the doors closed immediately behind her.

As the train started again in motion and clattered into the dark tunnel, Alice did not have the slightest idea where she was going. There was nothing to see out of the windows except the black tunnel walls, and for a moment she just sat and looked at her own reflection, which was strangely distorted by the curve of the glass. Her body was the same as she remembered, but her neck appeared to be stretched very long as if she had grown several inches. She laughed as she moved to her feet, to see that her body now seemed to stretch too in this weird and wonderful way, so that she appeared to be long and thin like a doll made out of rubber that was being pulled at both ends at the same time.

When Alice had tired of this game, she sat down and looked up again at the party poster that she had seen through the window. Next to it was an advertisement for the Notting Hill Carnival, and she wondered whether there was a connection between this and the Masked Ball. "I know that wearing masks is a big part of the tradition of carnival and that the Caribbean word 'Mas' relates to the word 'Masquerade'." she said to herself. "Here I go again!" she laughed. "I do wish I was as bookish as this when I was studying for exams!"

In an instant, she had made her decision: if she could find no other clues, she would travel to Notting Hill. There, she might spot the White Rabbit once again, but, in any case, it would be sure to be an adventure.

The train set off, soon pulling into a brightly lit station, where the doors slid open. After leaving the train and walking along a series of tunnels to change lines, Alice was on the Circle Line, and travelling north at great speed towards Notting Hill Gate.

There, she alighted. She had never been to the carnival before, but had heard a lot about it.

Alice knew that the Notting Hill Carnival had been held in London since 1966 each August Bank Holiday, and that this was the time of year when the streets of West London came alive with the sounds of Calypso, Reggae, R&B, Funk, and more recently House and Dubstep, and the smell of Afro-Caribbean cooking: jerk chicken, patties, and rice-and-peas (which strangely did not contain peas).

She found the station deserted however, though she could feel the throb of a pumping sub-bass coming from afar.

Alice wandered around the corridors of the station for quite sometime, trying to find the exit, and eventually found herself in a room that was restricted to railway staff. She knew this because there was a set of coat hooks just inside the door, on which was hanging a railway uniform jacket and hat, and, more significantly, a notice on the door that read 'STAFF ONLY'.

The room was long and narrow and had doors spaced along each wall but they were all locked. When Alice had been all the way down one side and up the other, trying every door, she was close to giving up, and found herself back at the coat hooks where she had started. Suddenly she noticed that from one of the hooks hung a lanyard with a tiny golden key tied to it, and Alice's first idea was that this might belong to one of the doors of the room; but alas! either the locks were too large, or the key was too small, but at any rate it would not open any of them.

However, on the second time round, she came upon something she had not noticed before. There it was again: another advertisement for the Masked Ball that had so fascinated her, but this time it was no larger than a Royal Mail postage stamp, stuck to a little door about fifteen inches high. She tried the little golden key in the lock, and to her great delight it fitted!

Alice opened the door and found that it led into a small passage, not much larger than a rat hole: she knelt down and looked along the passage, seeing that it was a tunnel arched with tiny brickwork that she knew she could never manage to fit through. A small bright green balloon tied with a red ribbon lay on the ground just inside the doorway, tantalising Alice into thinking that this door would somehow lead to the party. How she longed to follow her instincts, but she could not even get her head through the doorway; "and even if my head would go through," thought Alice, "it would be of very little use without my shoulders. Oh I wish I could shut myself up like a telescope! I think I could, if only I knew how to begin." For, you see, so many out-of-the-way things had happened lately, that Alice had begun to think that very few things indeed were really impossible.

There seemed to be no use in waiting by the little door, so she went back to the coat hooks, half hoping she might find another key, or at any rate a book of rules for shutting people up like telescopes.

This time, she spotted a shelf above the line of coat hooks with a little bottle on it, ("which certainly was not there before," said Alice), and tied round the neck of the bottle was a paper label, with the words 'DRINK ME' beautifully printed on it in large letters.

It was all very well to say "Drink me" but the wise little Alice was not going to do that in a hurry. "No, I'll look first," she said, "and see whether it's marked 'poison' or not", for she had read several nice little histories about people who had got into trouble, all because they *would* not remember the simple rules their friends had taught them: such as, if you used your mobile telephone in a petrol station, you might cause an explosion; and if you drove into the London Congestion Charge Zone on a week-day without paying, you were sure to be fined; and she had never forgotten that, if you drink much from a bottle marked 'poison' it is almost certain to disagree with you, sooner or later.

However, this bottle was *not* marked 'poison' so Alice ventured to taste it and finding it very nice, she very soon finished it off.

\* \* \*

"What a curious feeling!" said Alice. "I must be shutting up like a telescope."

And so it was indeed: she was now only ten inches high, and her face brightened up at the thought that she was now the right size for going through the little door to the party.

After a while, finding that nothing more happened, she decided on going through the little door at once; but, alas for poor Alice! when she got to the door she found she had forgotten the little golden key, and when she went back to the coat hooks, she found she could not possibly reach it. She could see it quite plainly hanging on the lanyard way above her, but the tiled wall was way too slippery to climb. She stood for a moment contemplating her dilemma.

"What is the answer?" she said aloud, half expecting to receive some sign that would help her with this riddle.

Just then there was a fierce wind and a low hum and rumble, which Alice quickly recognised as the sound of another underground train approaching. With sudden desperation, she began to run towards the sound, in the hope that this may, in some way, offer an alternative to the predicament she was in.

In her hurry, she quite forgot her diminutive size and was nearly blown away by the force of the wind sweeping along the passage. She reached the platform just as the train arrived.

The doors slid open like another invitation to board the train and, without thinking, Alice jumped on. It was quite a leap this time, across the dark span between the train and the platform edge, and for a moment Alice was in real danger of slipping into it, never to be seen again. Now Alice really understood why passengers were often warned to 'Mind the Gap!'

The doors closed behind her and the train set off. Alice began to try to climb up onto a seat but was soon so tired with the effort, the poor little thing sat down on the floor and cried.

"Come, there's no use in crying like that!" said Alice to herself, rather sharply; "I advise you to leave off this minute!" She generally gave herself very good advice, (though she very seldom followed it) and sometimes she scolded herself so severely to bring tears into her eyes; and once she remembered trying to box her own ears for cheating herself in a game of croquet she was playing against herself, for this curious child was very fond of pretending to be two people. "But it's no use now," thought poor Alice, "to pretend to be two people! Why there's hardly enough of me left to make one respectable person!"

She travelled for sometime sitting in this position on the floor of the carriage, below the priority seating that was reserved for elderly and disabled people and mothers. Finally the train came to a sudden halt. The doors slid open and she quickly jumped out, finding herself on another deserted station platform, this time at Piccadilly Circus. This struck Alice as very strange for two reasons: firstly because she remembered Piccadilly Circus to be one of the busiest stations she had ever seen – even late into the evening - and now it was silent and empty; and secondly, because she could not for the life of her remember changing from the Central line to the Bakerloo.

She began to follow the signs to the exit, which was quite a feat considering how small she was, though it did mean that she could walk easily under the barriers without being noticed.

She had finally reached the station's circular entrance hall, when she spotted ahead of her the White Rabbit, pausing to look at his pocket watch before hurrying on. He was standing directly in front of the World Clock, which was a most unique linear timepiece that had been set in the wall of the station in the 1920's, and something which Alice had not noticed before, even though she had been to the West End several times. For a moment, time seemed to stand still, though the central strip of the clock continued to move almost imperceptibly across the centre of the map of the world.

Then the Rabbit was on the move again, hurrying towards the station's exit onto Coventry Street. Meanwhile, Alice's eye fell on a little glass box that was lying under the clock: she opened it and found in it a very small cake, on which the words 'EAT ME' were beautifully marked in currants.

"Well, I'll eat it," said Alice, "and if it makes me grow larger, I can go back to Notting Hill Gate and reach that key on the hook, and if it makes me smaller, I can creep under the door; so either way I'll get into the passage and go to the party, and I don't care which happens." So she set to work and very soon finished off the cake, though shrewdly deciding to leave the station first.

## Chapter II
# The Pool of Tears in Trafalgar Square

"Curiouser and curiouser!" cried Alice (she was so much surprised, that for a moment she quite forgot how to speak good English); "now I'm opening out like the largest telescope that ever was!"

As she ascended the last steps bringing her up onto street level into the sunshine, she found that she was much taller than before. She could quite easily see over the heads of the pedestrians that hurried along Piccadilly.

"I wish I had been this size when I was at the Royal Academy Summer Exhibition a few weeks ago," she said, remembering how she had stood in a queue in the courtyard of Burlington House, not knowing how near to the front she was getting.

Now Alice could easily look into the windows of the top decks of the red London buses as they navigated past the statue of Anteros, and see the people staring back at her as if she was part of the fantastical show of advertisements and flashing lights that adorned the surrounding buildings.

In fact she was now more than nine feet high and was continuing to grow. She turned back to try to descend the steps into the Underground, thinking that her new size would make it very easy to return and retrieve that key. But it was as much as she could do, crouching down on hands and knees, to look into the entrance. To get back in was more hopeless than ever. She stood up again, dusted herself down, and in only a few paces she was striding along Haymarket and into the heart of theatre-land. She was now inadvertently stopping traffic - cars and lorries were honking their horns - and people were diving into shop doorways to try to avoid getting squashed by her immense weight. At one point, a group of policemen even tried to stop her progress by kettling her, but she simply stepped over the police cordon with one of her over-sized feet and continued towards Charing Cross.

In a few giant paces, she arrived in Trafalgar Square, where she found a bus shelter (which made a rather convenient seat) and, steadying herself by grabbing hold of Nelson's Column (which she could comfortably embrace with the fingers of one hand), sat down on its roof and began to cry again.

"You ought to be ashamed of yourself," said Alice, "A great girl like you," (she may well say this), "to go on crying in this way! Stop this moment, I tell you!"

But she went on all the same, shedding gallons of tears until there was a large pool all round her.

Things were quieter now and Alice guessed that the streets around her must have been closed to traffic. After a time she heard a little pattering of feet in the distance, and she hastily dried her eyes to see what was coming. It was the White Rabbit, splendidly dressed, with a pair of white kid gloves in one hand and a large fan in the other: he came trotting along the front of the National Gallery, cut diagonally across Trafalgar Square in the direction of the Royal Society of Arts in a great hurry, muttering to himself as he came, "Oh, the Duchess, the Duchess! Oh! Won't she be savage if I've kept her waiting!"

Alice felt so desperate that she was ready to ask help of anyone; so, when the Rabbit came near her, she began, in a low timid voice, "If you please, sir…"

The Rabbit started violently, dropped the white kid gloves and the fan, and changed direction dramatically to scurry away in the direction of Pall Mall, as hard as he could go.

Alice took up the fan and gloves and, as she was now very hot – she guessed this was because she was now closer to the sun - she kept fanning herself all the time she went on talking: "Dear, dear! How queer everything is today! And yesterday things went on just as usual. I wonder if I've been changed overnight? Let me think: was I the same when I got up this morning? I almost think I can remember feeling a little different. But if I'm not the same, the next question is, Who in the world am I? Ah, *that's* the great puzzle!"

As she said this she looked down at her hands and was surprised to see that she had put on one of the Rabbit's little white kid gloves while she was talking.

"How *can* I have done that?" she thought. "I must be growing small again." She jumped down from the bus shelter, which was now quite a drop, and went to a nearby post box to measure herself by it, and found that, as nearly as she could guess she was now two feet high, and was going on shrinking rapidly: she soon found out that the cause of this was the fan she was holding, and she dropped it hastily, just in time to avoid shrinking away altogether.

"That was a narrow escape!" said Alice, a good deal frightened at the sudden change, but very glad to find herself still in existence; "Now I can get back down into the Underground." She began to retrace her steps towards Shaftsbury Avenue, but ahead of her she could see a chain of policemen blocking the road, their arms linked to stem a swell of angry people behind them who were shouting and pointing towards her.

"Things are worse than ever," thought the poor little child.

As she said these words, her foot slipped, and in another moment, splash!

She was up to her chin in cold water. Her first idea was that she had somehow fallen into the Thames.

However, she soon made out that she was in one of the pools in Trafalgar Square, which was now overflowing from the tears she had wept when she was more than nine feet high.

"I wish I had not cried so much!" said Alice, as she swam about, trying to find her way out. "I shall be punished for it now, I suppose, by being drowned in my own tears! That *will* be a queer

thing, to be sure! However, everything is queer today!"

Just then she heard something splashing about in the pool a little way off, and she swam nearer to make out what it was; at first she thought it must be a walrus or a hippopotamus, but then she remembered how small she was now, and she soon made out that it was only a mouse that had slipped in like herself.

"Would it be of any use," thought Alice, "to speak to this mouse?" so she began: "Oh Mouse, do you know the way out of the pool? I am very tired of swimming about here, O Mouse." (Alice thought this must be the right way of speaking to a mouse: she had never done such a thing before, but she remembered having seen in her brother's Latin Grammar, 'A mouse – of a mouse – to a mouse – a mouse – O mouse!' The mouse looked at her rather inquisitively, and seemed to her to wink with one of its little eyes, but it said nothing.

"Perhaps it doesn't understand English," thought Alice, "I daresay it's a French mouse, come over with William the Conqueror." (For, with all her knowledge of history, Alice had no very clear notion how long ago anything happened.) So she began again, "Où est ma chatte?" which was the first sentence in her French lesson book. The mouse gave a sudden leap out of the water, and seemed to quiver all over with fright.

"Oh, I beg your pardon!" cried Alice hastily, afraid that she had hurt the poor animal's feelings. "I quite forgot you didn't like cats."

"Not like cats!" cried the mouse. "Would *you* like cats if you were me?"

"Well, perhaps not," said Alice in a soothing tone: "don't be angry about it. And yet I wish I could show you our cat Dinah: I think you'd take a fancy to cats if you could only see her. She is such a dear quiet thing," Alice went on, half to herself, as she swam lazily about in the pool, "and she sits purring so nicely by the fire, licking her paws and washing her face – and she is such a nice soft thing to nurse – and she's such a capital one for catching mice – oh, I beg your pardon!" cried Alice again, for this time the Mouse was bristling all over, and she felt certain it must be really offended. "We won't talk about her any more if you'd rather not."

"We, indeed!" cried the Mouse, who was trembling down to the end of his tail. "As if *I* would talk on such a subject! Our family always *hated* cats: nasty, low, vulgar things! Don't let me hear the name again!"

"I won't indeed!" said Alice, in a great hurry to change the subject of conversation. "Are you – are you fond – of – of dogs?" The Mouse did not answer, so Alice went on eagerly: "There is such a nice little dog near our house in Hendon I should like to show you! Quite near to where one can get the best salt beef! A little bright-eyed terrier, you know, with oh, such long curly brown hair! And it'll fetch things when you throw them, and it'll sit up and beg for its dinner, and all sorts of things – I can't remember half of them – and it belongs to a farmer, you know, and he says it's so useful, it's worth a hundred pounds! He says it kills all the rats and – oh dear!" cried Alice in a sorrowful tone, "I'm afraid I've offended it again!" For the Mouse was now swimming away from her as hard as it could go, and making quite a commotion in the pool as it went.

So she called softly after it, "Mouse dear! Do come back again, and we won't talk about cats or dogs either, if you don't like them!" When the Mouse heard this, it turned around and swam slowly back to her: its face was quite pale, and it said in a low trembling voice, "Let us get to the shore, and then I'll tell you my history, and you'll understand why it is I hate cats and dogs."

The pool was getting quite crowded with the birds and animals that had fallen into it and, alarmingly, the flood waters seemed to be rising. Suddenly, with a tidal surge, Alice lost sight of the Mouse altogether as she was washed out of Trafalgar Square along Whitehall, and was heading at great speed towards the Houses of Parliament. A number of Royal Horse Guards were swept along with her as she passed Horse Guards Parade, and she was rather thankful that it was not the day of the Trooping of the Colour, as there would have been many more casualties. The guards were swimming gallantly against the tide in order to save their horses.

As she was swept past the end of Downing Street, several policemen joined her in the water, along with a number of press photographers who, poised with cameras, had been waiting for the Prime Minister to emerge from Number Ten in order to make a statement about climate change and global warming.

There was quite a bit of debris floating along Whitehall now -

flags and poppy wreaths from the Cenotaph, a bicycle, a set of traffic lights, a sign for road works, some banners of protest against British foreign policy, and a number of umbrellas (it was never really wise to spend a day in London without one!). A travel card floated by her and Alice was quick thinking enough to grab it. Even in the midst of such chaos, she thought this might come in useful as she was becoming rather sick of fare-dodging on the pretext of following animals in and out of the tube.

The waters were subsiding as Alice finally reached Parliament Square. She dragged herself out of the water at the foot of a large bronze statue of Winston Churchill, just as Big Ben was striking two o'clock, and a number of other bemused and dishevelled characters followed her.

## Chapter III

# A Caucus Race and a Long Tale in Parliament Square

They were indeed a queer looking party that assembled on the bank - the birds with bedraggled feathers, the animals with their fur clinging close to them, guardsmen, civil servants, one or two tourists, and a press photographer, and all dripping wet, cross, and uncomfortable.

After a few minutes, however, it seemed quite natural to Alice to be talking familiarly to them, as if she had known them all her life. Indeed, she had quite a long argument with the Lory, who at last turned sulky, and would only say, "I'm older than you, and must know better", and this Alice would not allow without knowing how old it was, and, as the Lory positively refused to tell its age, there was no more to be said.

The main question of course was, how to get dry again: they had a consultation about this (this seemed to be the obvious thing to do, whilst standing in the shadow of Parliament).

"What is a consultation?" asked one of the tourists. "Why," said one of the civil servants. "It is a regulatory process by which the public's opinion on matters affecting them is sought."

"The opinions gathered seldom have any influence on the final decision made." added a newspaper reporter.

Before the civil servant had time to retort, a Junior Minister, whom Alice thought she recognised as seeing on 'Question Time' the previous week, and who remarkably resembled a pole-cat ferret, called out "Sit Down, all of you, and listen to me! I'll soon make you dry enough!"

They all sat down at once in a ring, with the Junior Minster in the middle. Alice kept her eyes anxiously fixed on him, for she felt sure she would catch a bad cold if she did not get dry very soon.

"Ahem!" said the Junior Minister with an important air. "Are you all ready? This is the driest thing I know. Silence all round please! The House of Commons is the lower house of the Parliament of the United Kingdom which, like the House of Lords (the upper house) meets in the Palace of Westminster. The Commons is a body consisting of 650 members, who are elected to represent constituencies until Parliament is dissolved. The Commons' functions are to consider, through debate, new laws and changes to existing ones, authorise taxes, and provide scrutiny of the policy and expenditure of the Government. The function of the House of Lords is to scrutinise Bills that have been approved by the House of Commons. It regularly reviews and amends Bills from the Commons. While it is unable to prevent Bills passing into law…"

"Why would it want to do that?" asked a Lory.

"Why would it want to do what?" said the Junior Minister.

"Prevent Bill passing into law, and who is Bill anyway?" said the Lory, getting rather cross.

"Bill is not a 'who', but a 'what'!" said the Junior Minister, and went on, "While it is unable to prevent Bills passing into law except in certain limited circumstances, it can delay Bills and force the Commons to reconsider its decisions."

"There you go again!" said the Lory. "Delay Bill's what? I can't follow this story at all!"

The Junior Minister looked weary as he turned to Alice and asked: "How are *you* getting on now my dear?"

"As wet as ever," said Alice in a melancholy tone: "it doesn't seem to dry me at all."

"In that case," said the Dodo solemnly, rising to its feet, "I move that the meeting adjourn, for the immediate adoption of more energetic remedies-"

"Speak English!" said the Eaglet. "I don't know the meaning of half those long words, and what's more, I don't believe you do either!" And the Eaglet bent down its head to hide a smile: some of the other birds tittered audibly.

"What I was going to say," said the Dodo in an offended tone, "was the best thing to get us dry is a Caucus race."

"What is a Caucus race?" said Alice.

"Why," said the Dodo, "the best way to explain it is to do it."

First it marked out a race-course, which took sometime because it incorporated most of Parliament Square, Westminster Bridge and Westminster Abbey, ("the exact shape doesn't matter," it said) and then all the party were placed along the course, here and there.

There was no 'one, two, three and away,' but they began running when they liked, and left off when they liked, so that it was not easy to know when the race was over.

Not wishing to be accused of not entering into the spirit of things, Alice ran for a while, but soon found she had lost the route of the race altogether and was nearing St James's Park. There, she spotted the Mouse again and caught up with it.

"You promised to tell me your history, you know," said Alice, "and why it is you hate – C and D," she added in a whisper, half afraid that it would be offended again.

"Mine is a long and sad tail!" said the Mouse, turning to Alice, and sighing.

"It is a long tail, certainly," said Alice, looking down with wonder at the Mouse's tail; "but why do you call it sad?" and she kept on puzzling about it while the Mouse was speaking, so that her idea of the tale was something like this:

"Fury said to a
mouse, that
he met in the
house, "Let

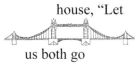

us both go
to law : *I*

will prosecute *you*. –
Come, I'll

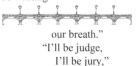

take no denial:

We must have
the trial;

For really
this morning
I've nothing

to do."
Said the

mouse to the cur,
"Such a trial, dear sir,
With no jury or judge,
would be wasting

our breath."
"I'll be judge,
I'll be jury,"

said cunning
old Fury: "I'll
try the whole cause

and condemn
you to
death."

"Couldn't you have got legal aid?" asked Alice.

"What?" said the Mouse.

"Legal aid is the provision of assistance to people otherwise unable to afford legal representation and access to the court system," said Alice, remembering a recent lesson she had attended in school on the history of the welfare state.

"I know what it is!" said the Mouse.

"Or you could have called one of those companies that represent you if you have sustained an injury but it was someone else's fault. My aunt once tripped over a loose paving stone outside a supermarket on the way to Bingo, and she was awarded £5000."

"You are not attending!" said the Mouse to Alice severely.

"I beg your pardon," said Alice very humbly: "you had got to the fifth bend I think?"

"I had not!" cried the Mouse sharply and very angrily.

"A knot!" said Alice, always ready to make herself useful, and looking anxiously about her. "Oh, do let me help to undo it!"

"I shall do nothing of the sort," said the Mouse, getting up and walking away. "You insult me by talking such nonsense!"

"I didn't mean it!" pleaded poor Alice. "But you're so easily offended, you know!"

The Mouse only growled in reply.

"Please come back and finish your story!" Alice called after it, but the Mouse only shook its head impatiently and walked a little quicker.

Finding herself alone in St James's Park, Alice began to walk across the grass. It was nice to have some peace and quiet and feel the sun on her face so that she could gather her thoughts for a moment. She walked for a while along the side of the lake, wondering if anyone at home was worrying about her whereabouts. She had a niggling feeling that she was in some way responsible for the destruction of a significant part of the capital and wondered if she might appear on the tea-time news.

"I'm sure I was not recognised by any of the reporters I met in the flood in any case," she thought. "But, if they had interviewed me, I would have said 'no comment'!" She had heard this said many a time, when someone was forced into a corner and was reluctant to speak. "Yes," she mused, "this must be the very kind of situation that would lead someone to declare 'no comment'." (She could not actually remember a time that was so similar to this, when Haymarket had been devastated by a giant and the whole of Whitehall had been flooded, but she soon put this thought out of her head.)

As she reached the other side of the park, she heard a little pattering of footsteps in the distance.

*Chapter IV*

# The Rabbit Sends in a Little Bill
# at Buckingham Palace

It was the White Rabbit, trotting slowly along the Mall and looking anxiously about it as it stood at the foot of the Duke of York Column. Alice found herself singing the old nursery rhyme: "Oh the Grand old Duke of York".

Her own thoughts about how the song depicted the drills that the Duke had introduced during the French revolutionary wars to reform the British Army into a capable modernised force were interrupted, when Alice heard the White Rabbit muttering to itself:

"The Duchess, the Duchess! Oh my fur and whiskers! She'll get me executed! Where can I have dropped them, I wonder?"

Alice guessed in a moment that it was looking for the fan and the pair of gloves, and she began searching for them.

Just then there was a screech of tyres on tarmac, and she saw that the White Rabbit had hailed a black taxi cab and was climbing into the back of it. Not wishing to be left behind, Alice, who was still only a few inches high, ran across the road and was just in time to grab the rear bumper, before the taxi took off at what seemed to be a phenomenal pace.

The taxi went hurtling along the Mall, and she felt sure that if there had been any speed cameras, the vehicle would have been caught on film, with her hanging from the rear. What a strange picture that would have been!

It was all she could do to cling onto the bumper as the car proceeded towards Buckingham Palace, where upon it circled the large Victoria Memorial and then drove straight through the open gates, with the Queen's guards standing to attention, looking very formal in their red tunics and black bearskins.

Alice noticed as she neared the huge imposing building that the flag was flying at full mast, which indicated that the Queen was at home.

For a moment, Alice wondered how she could really be in this current predicament: only a few inches high and clinging to the bumper of a black taxi cab. "I certainly do not feel at all myself today," she said. "Maybe I have turned into the Alice that went to see the Queen with Christopher Robin!"

The taxi pulled up at a side entrance – she fleetingly hoped that it would draw into the Royal Mews, which housed all the carriages for royal and state occasions.

Through the rear window, Alice watched as the Rabbit paid the fare and got out of the vehicle. It suddenly noticed little Alice standing behind the car, dishevelled and shaken from her terrifying ride.

"Why Mary Ann, what *are* you doing out here? Run in this moment, and fetch me a pair of gloves and a fan!"

And Alice was so much frightened that she ran off in the direction it pointed to, without trying to explain the mistake it had made.

"He took me for his housemaid," she said to herself as she ran. "How surprised he'll be when he finds out who I am! But I'd better take his fan and gloves – that is, if I can find them."

She went into the side door of the palace without knocking and hurried up the stairs, in great fear lest she should meet the real Mary Ann – or indeed the Queen of England – and be turned out of the palace before she had found the fan and gloves.

"How queer it seems," Alice said to herself, "to be running errands for a rabbit! I suppose Dinah'll be sending me on errands next!" And she began fancying the sort of thing that would happen: " 'Miss Alice! Come here directly, and get ready for your walk!' 'Coming in a minute, nurse! But I've got to watch this mouse-hole till Dinah comes back, and see that the mouse doesn't get out.' Only I don't think," Alice went on, "that they'd let Dinah stop in the house if it began ordering people about like that!"

By this time, she found her way to a rather elegant state room with a table by the window, and on it (as she had hoped) a fan and two or three pairs of tiny white kid gloves.

She took up the fan and a pair of gloves and was just about to leave the room when her eye fell upon a little bottle that stood near the looking glass.

There was no label this time with the words 'DRINK ME', but nevertheless she uncorked it and put it to her lips.

"I know something interesting is sure to happen," she said to herself. "I do hope it'll make me grow large again, for I'm really tired of being such a tiny little thing!"

It did so indeed, and much sooner than she had expected: before she had drunk half the bottle, she found her head pressing against the ceiling, and had to stoop to save her neck from being broken.

She hastily put down the bottle, saying to herself, "That's quite enough - I hope I shan't grow any more - as it is I can't get out of the door - I do wish I hadn't drunk so much!"

Alas! It was too late for that. She went on growing and growing and as a last resource, she put one arm out of the window and one arm up the chimney.

Luckily for Alice, the little magic bottle had taken its full effect, and she grew no larger, but she was slightly unnerved to see that a CCTV camera fastened to a lamp post outside had angled itself to focus entirely on the window out of which her arm was projecting.

"It was much pleasanter at home," thought poor Alice, "when one wasn't always growing larger and smaller, and being ordered about by mice and rabbits. I almost wish I hadn't followed the rabbit down to Knightsbridge tube station – and yet – and yet – it's rather curious, you know, this sort of life! I do wonder what can have happened to me! When I used to read fairy tales, I fancied that kind of thing never happened, and now here I am in the middle of one! I really should start to write a blog. This would make a great production at the Royal Opera House or any theatre. There ought to be a book written about me, that there ought! And when I grow up, I'll write one – but I'm grown up now," she added in a sorrowful tone; "at least there's no room to grow up any *more* here."

"But then," thought Alice, "shall I *never* get any older than I am now? That'll be a comfort, one way – never to be an old woman – but then – always to have lessons to learn! Oh, I shouldn't like *that*!"

"Oh, you foolish Alice!" she answered herself. "How can you learn lessons in here? Why, there's hardly room for *you*, and no room at all for any lesson books!"

And so she went on, taking first one side and then the other, and making quite a conversation of it altogether; but after a few minutes she heard a voice outside, and stopped to listen.

"Mary Ann! Mary Ann!" said the voice. "Fetch me my gloves this moment!" Then came a pattering of feet on stairs. Alice knew it was the Rabbit coming to look for her, and she trembled till she shook the whole wing of the palace, quite forgetting that she was now about a thousand times larger than the Rabbit, and had no reason to be afraid of it.

Presently, the Rabbit came up to the door and tried to open it; but as the door opened inwards, and Alice's elbow was pressed hard against it, that attempt proved a failure. Alice heard it say to itself "Then I'll go round and get in at the window."

"That you won't!" thought Alice, and, after waiting till she fancied she heard the Rabbit just under the window, she suddenly spread out her hand, and made a snatch in the air. She did not get hold of anything, but she heard a little shriek and a fall, and a crash of broken glass, from which she concluded that it was just possible that it had fallen into a cucumber-frame, or something of the sort.

"Would the Queen keep cucumbers, I wonder?" Alice mused.

"Next came an angry voice she had not heard before, "Philip. Philip dear! Come and look at this! What is it that is in that window?"

"Why, it's an arm!" came the answer from a very well-spoken gentleman.

"An arm? Who ever saw one that size? Why it fills the whole window!"

"Sure, it does, but it's an arm all the same."

"Well, it's got no business there! Guards!"

There was a long silence after this, followed by a number of whispered voices. At last she spread out her hand again and made a little snatch at the air. This time there were more shrieks and more sounds of broken glass.

"What a number of cucumber frames there must be!" thought Alice. "I wonder what they'll do next! As for pulling me out of the window, I only wish they *could*! I'm sure I don't want to stay in here any longer!"

She waited some time without hearing anything more: at last came a rumbling of little cartwheels and the sound of a good many voices all talking together: she made out the words: "Where's the other ladder? – Why, I hadn't to bring but one; Bill's got the other – Bill! fetch it here! – Here put 'em up at this corner – No, tie 'em together first – they don't reach half high enough yet – Oh! they'll do well enough; don't be particular – Here Bill! catch hold of this rope – Will the roof bear? – Mind that loose slate – Oh it's coming down! Heads below!" (a loud crash) – "Now, who did that? – It was Bill, I fancy – Who's to go down the chimney? – Nay, I shan't! *You* do it! – That I won't, then! Bill's to go down – Here, Bill! You're to go down the chimney!"

"Oh! So Bill's got to come down the chimney, has he?" said Alice to herself. "Why, they seem to put everything upon Bill! I wouldn't be in Bill's place for a good deal: this fireplace is narrow, to be sure; but I *think* I can kick a little!"

Alice wondered fleetingly if this was the Bill to which the Junior Minister had been referring earlier.

She drew her foot as far down the chimney as she could, and waited till she heard something scratching and scrambling about in the chimney close above her: then, saying to herself "This is Bill," she gave one sharp kick, and waited to see what would happen next.

The first thing she heard was a general chorus of "There goes Bill!" then the Rabbit's voice alone, "Catch him, you by the hedge!" then silence, and then another confusion of voices – "Hold up his head – Brandy now – Don't choke him – How was it? What happened to you? Tell us all about it. Should we send in Harry? Maybe he would have better luck?"

Last came a feeble reply, "Well, I hardly know - all I know is, something came at me like a Jack-in-a-box, and up I went like a sky-rocket!"

After a minute or two, they began moving about again, and Alice heard the Rabbit say "A barrowful will do, to begin with."

"A barrowful of what?" thought Alice. But she had not long to doubt, for the next moment a shower of little pebbles came rattling in at the window, and some of them hit her in the face.

"I'll put a stop to this," she said to herself, and shouted out, "You'd better not do that again!" There was a dead silence outside instantly.

Alice noticed with some surprise that the pebbles were turning into little cupcakes as they lay on the floor, and a bright idea came into her head.

33

"If I eat one of these cakes," she thought, "it's sure to make *some* change in my size."

So she swallowed one of the cakes, and was delighted to find that she began shrinking directly. As soon as she was small enough to get through the door, she ran out of the palace, and found quite a crowd of animals and people waiting outside. They all made a rush at Alice the moment she appeared; but she ran off as hard as she could go, and was soon out of the palace gates.

"The first thing I've got to do," said Alice to herself, "is to grow to my right size again, and the second thing is to find my way to the Masked Ball."

It sounded an excellent plan, and very neatly and simply arranged.

The only difficulty was, that she had not the smallest idea how to set about it; and, while she was peering about in the trees, a little sharp bark just over her head made her look up in a great hurry.

An enormous Corgi puppy was looking down at her with large round eyes, and stretching out one paw, trying to touch her.

"Poor little thing!" Said Alice, in a coaxing tone, though she was very frightened that it might be hungry, in which case it would be very likely to eat her up, in spite of all her coaxing.

Hardly knowing what she did, she picked up a little stick and held it out to the puppy; whereupon the puppy jumped into the air off all its feet at once, with a yelp of delight, and rushed at the stick.

Alice dodged behind a large thistle to keep herself from being run over; and, the moment she appeared at the other side, the puppy made another rush at the stick and tumbled head over heals in its hurry to get hold of it; then Alice, thinking it was very like having a game with a cart-horse, and expecting every moment to be trampled under its feet, ran round the thistle again; then the puppy began a series of short charges at the stick, running a very little way forwards each time and a long way back, and barking all the while, till at last it sat down a good way off, panting, with its tongue hanging out of its mouth, and its great eyes half shut.

This seemed a good opportunity for making her escape so she set off at once towards the street, and, spotting a double-decker bus, jumped onto the back of it as it moved along Park Lane. The puppy's bark soon sounded quite faint in the distance.

"Oh dear!" said Alice, "I'd nearly forgotten that I've got to grow up again. I suppose I ought to eat or drink something but the question is, what?"

She travelled for some miles, clinging onto the pole for fear that she may very well fall off the open platform at the back of the bus, while she considered what she might do next.

She was now travelling along the Edgware Road, and there seemed no limit to the choices of places to eat there: Mediterranean, Middle Eastern, Indian... the list went on and on.

At the next available stop, Alice jumped off the bus. The road was unusually quiet, and the seats outside the cafés were empty. This was particularly strange since London's implementation of a smoking ban in 2007, outlawing smoking in all enclosed public places, which had resulted in smokers gathering outside buildings in droves to smoke in all weathers.

However, in the near-deserted street, Alice came to a Shisha Café, outside of which was a table occupied by a large blue caterpillar, who was sitting with its arms folded, quietly smoking a long hookah, and taking not the smallest notice of her or anything else.

She was not so familiar with the origins of shisha, but had read that it hailed from India, Persia, or Turkey. She stretched herself up on tiptoe – she was still only a few inches high - and peeped over the edge of the seat on which the caterpillar was sitting to get a closer look.

She watched as the caterpillar topped up his pipe with charcoal before sitting back and inhaling deeply. He blew out a plume of thick smoke which held the overpowering aroma of strawberries.

## Chapter V

# Advice from a Caterpillar
# on the Edgware Road

The Caterpillar and Alice looked at each other for some time in silence: at last, the Caterpillar took the hookah out of its mouth and addressed her in a languid, sleepy voice.

"Who are *you*?" said the Caterpillar.

Alice replied rather shyly, "I-I hardly know, sir, just at present – at least I knew who I was when I got up this morning, but I think I have changed several times since then."

"What do you mean by that?" said the Caterpillar, sternly. "Explain yourself!"

"I can't explain *myself*, I'm afraid sir," said Alice. "because I'm not myself, you see."

"I don't see," said the Caterpillar.

"I'm afraid I can't put it more clearly," Alice replied very politely, "for I can't understand it myself to begin with; and being so many different sizes in a day is very confusing."

"It isn't," said the Caterpillar.

"Well, perhaps you haven't found it so yet," said Alice; "but when you have to turn into a chrysalis – you will some day, you know – and then after that into a butterfly, I should think you'll feel it a little queer, won't you?"

"Not a bit," said the Caterpillar.

"Well, perhaps your feelings may be different," said Alice; "all I know is, it would feel very queer to *me*."

"You!" said the Caterpillar contemptuously. "Who are *you*?"

Which brought them back again to the beginning of the conversation. Alice felt a little irritated at the Caterpillar's making such very short remarks, and she drew herself up and said, very gravely, "I think you ought to tell me who *you* are, first."

"Why?" said the Caterpillar.

Here was another puzzling question; and as Alice could not think of any good reason, and as the Caterpillar seemed to be in a very unpleasant state of mind, she turned away and began to walk further along the Edgware Road.

"Come back!" the Caterpillar called after her. "I've something important to say!"

This sounded promising, certainly: Alice turned and came back again.

"Keep your temper," said the Caterpillar.

"Is that all?" said Alice, swallowing down her anger as well as she could.

"No," said the Caterpillar.

Alice thought she might as well wait, as she had nothing else to do, and perhaps after all it might tell her something worth hearing.

For some minutes it puffed away without speaking, but at last it unfolded its arms, took the hookah out of its mouth again, and said, "So you think you're changed, do you?"

"I'm afraid I am, sir," said Alice; "I can't remember things as I used to – and I don't keep the same size for more than ten minutes together."

"Can't remember *what* things?" said the Caterpillar.

"Well. I've tried to say '*How doth the little busy bee*', but it all came different!" Alice replied in a very melancholy voice.

"Repeat, '*You are old, Father Thames*'," said the Caterpillar.

Alice folded her hands, and began:

*"You are old Father Thames," the young man said,*
*"And your water has turned very brown;*
*Though I cannot see right down to your river bed,*
*Why are you still toast of the town?"*

*"In my youth," said the river, "circa 50AD,"*
*Londinium was built as a port,*
*Ever since then, I've attracted debris*
*Far more than ever I ought.*

*As it grew to a size, the city dumped waste:*
*and my colour just turned black as ink*
*The House of Commons adjourned in great haste*
*In the days of the famous 'Great Stink'.*

*It got to a point when it couldn't get worse,*
*And diseases did people contract.*

*When even Prince Albert was wheeled in a hearse*
*It was sure time to clean up my act.*

*As world trade grew, I was worthy of note,*
*and my docks were as busy as bees;*
*For so many things were transported by boat,*
*and London ruled the high seas.*

*But you ask me, why ever I still am the toast*
*Of the town, well it isn't a mystery:*
*I am simply the lifeline if I had to boast*
*and a large part of this city's history!"*

"That is not said right," said the Caterpillar.

"Not *quite* right, I'm afraid, said Alice, timidly. "Some of the words have got altered."

"It is wrong from beginning to end. You've made no mention of the great Jubilee river pageant of 2012, or the London Olympics!" said the Caterpillar decidedly, and there was a silence for some minutes.

The Caterpillar was the first to speak.

"What size do you want to be?" he asked.

"Oh I am not particular as to size," Alice hastily replied; "only one doesn't like changing so often, you know."

"I *don't* know," said the Caterpillar.

Alice said nothing: she had never been so contradicted in all her life before, and she felt that she was losing her temper.

"Well I should like to be a *little* larger, sir, if you wouldn't mind," said Alice; "three inches is such a wretched height to be."

"It is a very good height indeed!" said the Caterpillar angrily, rearing itself upright as it spoke (it was exactly three inches high). "There are lots of very good things that are small: a mobile telephone, a DVD, a lottery ticket…"

"But I'm not used to it!" pleaded poor Alice in a piteous tone. And she thought to herself, "I wish the creatures wouldn't be so easily offended!"

"You'll get used to it in time," said the Caterpillar; and it put the hookah into its mouth and began smoking again.

This time Alice waited patiently until it chose to speak again. In a minute or two the Caterpillar took the hookah out of its mouth and yawned once or twice, and shook itself. Then it got down off the chair, and began to crawl away along the Edgware Road, merely remarking as it went, "One side will make you grow taller, and the other side will make you shorter."

"One side of what? the other side of what?" thought Alice to herself.

"Of the mushroom," said the Caterpillar, just as if she had asked out loud; and in another moment he was out of sight.

"What could it mean?" Alice wondered. It sounded like it must be talking about a pretty big mushroom if one side of it could make one grow taller whilst the other side could make one smaller. "Where would I find a big mushroom like that in London?"

She knew that there were mushroom-like acoustic panels on the ceiling of the Royal Albert Hall, which had been installed in 1969 to solve the problem of the giant echo in the building. But she was pretty sure that they were not edible. The biggest mushroom-like structure she could think of was the Millennium Dome, which spanned 365 metres – one metre for every day of the year – but she knew that it was made of steel and tensioned fabric and was not in the slightest bit appetising.

She had heard of 'magic mushrooms' but since they had been legislated as a Class A drug, the wise little Alice did not want to go looking for them. She had had more than enough excitement already without risking going to prison for seven years.

At a loss for a moment, Alice suddenly decided to head for Camden. She knew that one could get weird and wonderful things in the market there, and that someone would be sure to help her.

She hopped on another passing bus, and was soon travelling East on a number 27 along Marylebone Road. She clutched the hand rail in her arms for fear of being thrown off the open platform, as the red Routemaster moved from one stop to the next. Despite her diminutive size, she could still see out of the side, as the bus passed Baker Street, and then the big green dome that she still remembered as the London Planetarium, and next to it the famous wax-works, where a queue of tourists were standing outside waiting to be admitted.

Just short of the British Library and Kings Cross Station, the bus turned left and proceeded along Hampstead Road for a while, until Alice caught sight of Camden Town and made a brave jump down to the pavement.

## Chapter VI

# Pig and Pepper in Camden Town

Camden was a fascinating place, full of curiosity shops and intriguing distractions. Alice knew that one could get almost anything there, from a pair of steam-punk goggles to a bird cage. As she was still only three inches high, no-one seemed to notice her as she walked amongst the stalls in the market, looking at vintage clothing, scented candles, and the coolest accessories she had ever seen. Top hats, pocket watches, packs of cards, and everything you could ever want for a fancy dress party was there.

After a while, Alice found herself in a dark cobbled area of the market, where several food sellers were stirring huge steaming pots of food and calling to passers-by to stop and sample them. The food smelled good, and made her feel hungry. She continued for some way before finding a door that led into a large kitchen, which was full of smoke from one end to the other.

The Duchess, who reminded her of a pantomime dame she had seen in a show at the London Palladium, was sitting on a three-legged stool in the middle, nursing a baby. There was a cook leaning over a fire, stirring a large cauldron which seemed to be full of soup.

"What sort of soup is this?" said Alice.

"Why, mushroom of course," replied the cook, without looking up and, at this, Alice suddenly noticed that practically every surface in the kitchen was covered with mushrooms, which were piled high on chopping boards, in colanders and bowls.

"There's certainly too much pepper in that soup!" Alice said to herself, as well as she could for sneezing. There was certainly too much of it in the air. Even the Duchess sneezed occasionally and the baby was sneezing and howling alternately without a moment's pause.

The only two things in the kitchen that did not sneeze were the cook and a large cat which was sitting on the hearth grinning from ear to ear.

"Please would you tell me," said Alice rather timidly, "why your cat grins like that?"

'It's a Cheshire cat,' said the Duchess, "and that's why."

And with that she began nursing her child, singing a sort of lullaby to it as she did so:

*"Speak roughly to your little boy,*
*and beat him when he sneezes:*
*He only does it to annoy,*
*because he knows it teases."*

CHORUS
(In which the cook and the baby joined):
*"Wow! Wow! Wow!"*

While the Duchess sang the second verse of the song, she kept tossing the baby violently up and down, and the poor little thing howled so, that Alice could hardly hear the words:-

*"I speak severely to my boy,*
*I beat him when he sneezes;*
*For he can thoroughly enjoy*
*The pepper when he pleases!"*

CHORUS
*"Wow! Wow! Wow!"*

"How strange that the Caterpillar should talk about mushrooms earlier," she thought. "It is almost as if he knew."

Though Alice was cautious about eating strange mushrooms, she supposed that if they were in a kitchen being prepared for soup (even in Camden), and in light of the curious things that had already happened, they could do no harm.

Alice climbed up onto the table – this was a challenge in itself – and picked up the biggest mushroom she could find and broke off a bit with each hand.

"Oh, just help yourself!" said the Duchess, with a certain degree of sarcasm.

Alice was trying to remember what the Caterpillar had said to her: "One side will make you grow taller, and the other side will make you shorter."

"And now which is which?" she said to herself, and nibbled a little of the right-hand side to try the effect.

The next moment she felt a violent blow underneath her chin: it had struck her foot!

She was a good deal frightened by this very sudden change, but she felt that there was no time to be lost, as she was shrinking rapidly; so she set to work at once to eat some of the other bit.

Her chin was pressed so closely against her foot, that there was hardly room to open her mouth; but she did it at last, and managed to swallow a morsel of the left-hand bit.

She set to work very carefully, nibbling first at one piece and then at the other, until she had succeeded in bringing herself to her usual height.

It was so long since she had been anything near the right size, that it felt quite strange at first; but she got used to it in a few minutes, and began talking to herself, as usual. "How puzzling all these changes are! I'm never sure what I'm going to be, from one minute to another! However, I've got back to my right size: the next thing is to find out where the Masked Ball is going to take place. How is that to be done, I wonder?"

"Here! You may nurse the baby for a bit if you like!" the Duchess said to Alice, flinging the baby at her as she spoke without noticing that Alice was now significantly larger than before. "I have had an invitation to play charity croquet with the queen and I must get ready," and she hurried out of the room.

Alice caught the baby with some difficulty as it was a queer shaped creature, and held out its arms and legs in all directions, "just like a star-fish" thought Alice. The poor little thing was snorting like a steam engine when she caught it, and kept doubling itself up and straightening itself out again so that altogether, for the first minute or two, it was as much as she could do to hold it.

As soon as she had made out the proper way of nursing it (which was to twist it up into a sort of knot, and then keep tight hold of its right ear and left foot, so as to prevent its undoing itself), she carried it out into the open air.

"If I don't take this child away with me," thought Alice, "they're sure to kill it in a day or two: wouldn't it be murder to leave it behind?" She said the last words out loud, and the little thing grunted in reply (it had left off sneezing by this time).

"Don't grunt," said Alice, "that's not at all a proper way of expressing yourself."

The baby grunted again, and Alice looked very anxiously into its face to see what was the matter with it. There could be no doubt that it had a *very* turn-up nose, much more like a snout than a real nose; also its eyes were getting extremely small for a baby: altogether Alice did not like the look of the thing at all.

"But perhaps it was only sobbing," she thought, and looked into its eyes again, to see if there were any tears.

No, there were no tears. "If you're going to turn into a pig, my dear," said Alice, seriously, "I'll have nothing more to do with you. Mind now!" The poor little thing sobbed again (or grunted, it was impossible to say which), and they went on for some while in silence.

Alice was just beginning to think to herself, "Now, what am I to do with this creature when I get home?" when it grunted again, so violently that she looked down into its face with some alarm. There could be no mistake: it was neither more nor less than a pig, and she felt it would be quite absurd for her to carry it any further.

So she set the creature down and felt quite relieved to see it trot away quietly in amongst the stalls of Camden market. "If it had grown up," she said to herself, "it would have made a dreadfully ugly child: but it makes rather a handsome pig, I think." And she began thinking over other children she knew, who might do very well as pigs, when she was a little startled by seeing the Cheshire Cat sitting on a window sill a few yards off. Just a few inches from where it was sitting, Alice noticed that on the wall next to it was another poster advertising the Masked Ball. She had almost completely forgotten about her search for this, but now suddenly remembered that it was this that had led her into more recent predicaments. The cat grinned when it saw Alice. It looked good-natured, she thought: still it had very long claws and a great many teeth, so she felt that it ought to be treated with respect.

"Cheshire Puss," she began, rather timidly, as she did not at all know whether it would like the name: however, it only grinned a little wider. "Come, its pleased so far," thought Alice, as she went on. "Would you tell me if you know about the Masked Ball advertised on this poster?"

"Something and nothing," replied the Cheshire cat rather unhelpfully.

"Well, you are sitting right next to it," said Alice.

"And you are standing right next to the statue of a horse, but do you know anything about *that*?" said the Cat.

"Well, I suppose I don't," said Alice, suddenly aware that there was not just one statue of a horse but a number, all in different positions, as if they were riding out of the walls of the market.

"What is the significance of the horses?" said Alice, allowing herself to be distracted for a moment.

"It's the Stables Market," said the Cat in a tone that implied that this was obvious, "built on the site of the stables and horse hospital, which served the horses that pulled vehicles along the road, and the barges along the canal."

"Well, that's very interesting, but it doesn't answer *my* question," said Alice, remembering her point. "What do you know about the Masked Ball?"

"Something and nothing," the Cheshire Cat repeated.

"You've already said that!" She had upset a Mouse, been bored nearly to death by a Junior Minister, had been given some very cryptic advice from a Caterpillar, and had had a very close encounter with a pig already today; she was certainly in no mood for more games.

"The something I know is that you will not get in without an invitation," said the Cat.

"I have one!" declared Alice jubilantly, digging into her pocket and fishing out a screwed up piece of paper that was still a little wet from the Whitehall flood. She flattened it out across the palm of her hand and proudly showed the Cat.

"So you have," said the Cat, without emotion.

"So where is it?" asked Alice.

"Where is what?" said the Cat.

"THE MASKED BALL" said Alice with impatience.

"That is the nothing that I know," said the Cat conclusively, and added, "keep your temper."

"How am I ever going to find out?" Alice said with a slight tremble of desperation in her voice.

"You can ask anyone around here," suggested the Cat.

"Will anyone know?" asked Alice.

49

"Probably not. We're all mad," said the Cat. "I'm mad, you're mad."

"How do you know I'm mad?" said Alice.

"You must be," said the Cat, "or you wouldn't have come here."

Just then a pair of punk rockers walked past her, each with hair painted a different colour, which stood alarmingly on end.

"I do see what you mean now," said Alice.

"To begin with," said the Cat, "a dog's not mad. You grant that?"

Alice considered this for a moment, remembering Noel Coward's song about mad dogs and Englishmen going out in the midday sun, and wondered briefly if she could be included in this categorisation; but remembering that she had seen Big Ben strike two with her own eyes, she was pretty sure that it was now comfortably well into the afternoon, unless the clock was running backwards.

"I suppose so," said Alice.

"Well then," the Cat went on, "you see a dog growls when it's angry, and wags its tail when it's pleased. Now I growl when I'm pleased, and wag my tail when I'm angry. Therefore I'm mad!"

"*I* call it purring, not growling," said Alice.

"Call it what you like," said the Cat.

The Cat smiled and then vanished, and Alice was left alone to ponder what to do next. She felt no nearer to discovering the whereabouts of the Masked Ball, and she began to walk away from the market and was soon wondering aimlessly along the tow path of the Regents Canal to nowhere in particular, and watching the narrowboats in their bright painted colours, scoring lines across the water.

Not much time had passed before she found she had come to Regents Park, and was climbing the steps to the street and crossing into the Inner Circle to walk across the grass.

## Chapter VII

# A Mad Take-away in Regents Park

There was a table set out under a tree, covered with the remnants of what appeared to be a very large Indian take-away: there were aluminium containers of half-eaten curry, tandoori chicken, pilau rice, vegetable samosas, onion bhajis, naan bread, lime pickle, mango chutney, and a generous pile of popadoms. A March Hare and a Hatter were dining at it. A dormouse was sitting between them, fast asleep, and the other two were using it as a cushion, resting their elbows on it and talking over its head.

The table was large but the three were all crowded together at one corner of it.

"No room! No room!" they cried out when they saw Alice coming.

"There's *plenty* of room!" said Alice indignantly, and she sat down in a large arm-chair at one end of the table.

"I love Indian food!" said Alice.

"It's Pakistani," said the Hatter.

"Oh, I do beg your pardon," said Alice.

"Would you like a mango lassi?" asked the March Hare in an encouraging tone.

Alice looked all around the table for a jug or a bottle but there was nothing on it but food. "I don't see any mango lassi, do you have some?" she remarked.

"No, there isn't any," said the March Hare.

"Then it wasn't very civil of you to offer it," said Alice angrily.

"It wasn't very civil of you to sit down without being invited," said the March Hare.

"I didn't know it was *your* table," said Alice; "it's laid for a great many more than three."

"The Hatter has a tendency to over-order," said the March Hare. "Anyway, we can't eat anything because we have no chop-sticks."

"You don't eat Indian food with chopsticks," said Alice.

"Good, because this is Pakistani," said the March Hare.

"Your hair wants cutting," said the Hatter. He had been looking at Alice for some time with great curiosity.

"You should learn not to make personal remarks," Alice said with severity; "it's very rude."

The Hatter opened his eyes very wide on hearing this; but all he *said* was, "Why is a raven like a writing desk?"

"Come, we shall have some fun now!" thought Alice. "I'm glad they've begun asking riddles. –I believe I can guess that," she added aloud.

"Do you mean that you think you can find out the answer to it?" said the March Hare.

"Exactly so," said Alice.

"Then you should say what you mean," the March Hare went on.

"I do," Alice hastily replied; "at least I mean what I say – that's the same thing, you know."

"Not the same thing a bit!" said the Hatter. "You might just as well say that 'I see what I eat' is the same as 'I eat what I see'!"

"You might just as well say," added the March Hare, " 'that I like what I get' is the same thing as 'I get what I like'!"

"You might just as well say," added the Dormouse, who seemed to be talking in his sleep, "that 'I breathe when I sleep' is the same thing as 'I sleep when I breathe'!"

"It is the same thing with you," said the Hatter, and here the conversation dropped, and the party sat silent for a minute, while Alice thought over all she could remember about ravens and writing-desks, which wasn't much.

The Hatter was first to break the silence. "What day of the month is it?" he said, turning to Alice: he had taken his mobile telephone out of his pocket, and was looking at it uneasily, shaking it every now and then, and holding it to his ear.

Alice considered a little, and then said, "The fourth."

"Two days wrong!" sighed the Hatter. "I told you butter wouldn't suit the mechanism!" he added looking angrily at the March Hare.

"It was the best butter," the March Hare meekly replied.

"Yes, but some crumbs must have got in it as well," the Hatter grumbled: "you shouldn't have put it in with the bread-knife."

The March Hare took the mobile 'phone and looked at it gloomily. "Did you switch it off and on again?"

"Yes, yes, I did all that," said the Hatter.

"Did you press *Control – Alt - Delete*?"

"Yes."

"Did you download or upgrade?"

"I've tried everything."

Suddenly the telephone sprang into life with a strange chime that sounded like the bell of Big Ben, only very distorted as if it was somehow melting. The March Hare answered it.

"It's for you," said the March Hare, passing the device to Alice. She put it to her ear.

"It was the *best* butter, you know," the March Hare repeated to the Hatter.

Alice could hear nothing from the telephone but crackling.

"The dormouse is asleep again," said the Hatter and he picked up an onion bhaji and nudged it against the mouse's nose. The dormouse shook his head impatiently, and said without opening its eyes. "Of course, of course; just what I was going to remark myself."

Alice was getting impatient with holding the 'phone. "All I can hear is cracking," she said, giving the phone back to the March Hare.

"That's all I could hear," said the March Hare.

"Then how did you know it was for me?" asked Alice.

"Well it wasn't going to be for me, now was it," said the March Hare. "I mean, it's not *my* phone!"

Alice felt terribly puzzled.

"This reminds me of a little poem I once penned," said the Hatter.

"Oh do recite it!" said the March Hare.

"Yes do!" echoed the Dormouse.

The Hatter took little persuasion, and cleared his throat to begin:

*"I wanted to write to my lover*
*but even before I began*
*to select some choice words for my sweetheart,*
*my computer had thwarted my plan.*

*I was thinking of writing a poem,*
*adorned with clip-art of a rose,*
*but the programme encountered a problem*
*and said that it needed to close.*

*I intended to ask her to dinner*
*and tell her the time to come round,*
*but the IP address had a conflict*
*and the network path could not be found.*

*I wanted to propose to her marriage,*
*feeling sure it was well worth the risk,*
*but a system device was not ready,*
*and there was not enough space on the disk.*

*Frustrated by all of these errors*
*that were causing an ache in my head,*
*I logged out and then forced a shut down*
*and decided to ring her instead.*

*The call went straight to voice-mail..."*

The others applauded, and the Hatter made a little bow.
"Take some more food. Have you tried the chicken tikka masala?"
the March Hare said to Alice, very earnestly.
"I've had nothing yet," Alice replied in an offended tone, "so I
can't take more."
"You mean you can't take *less*," said the Hatter: "it's very easy to
take *more* than nothing."
"Nobody asked *your* opinion," said Alice.
"Who's making personal remarks now?" the Hatter asked
triumphantly.

Alice did not quite know what to say to this: so she helped herself to a vegetable samosa. She ate one and slipped another into her pocket for later.

"Have you guessed the riddle yet?" the Hatter said, turning to Alice again.

"No, I give up, what's the answer?" asked Alice.

"I haven't the slightest idea," said the Hatter.

"Nor I," said the March Hare.

Alice sighed wearily, "I think you might do something better than waste time in asking riddles that have no answers."

"If you knew Time as well as I do," said the Hatter, "you wouldn't talk about wasting *it*. It's *him*.'"

"I don't know what you mean," said Alice.

"Of course you don't!" the Hatter said, tossing his head contemptuously. "I dare say you have never even spoken to Time!"

"Perhaps not," Alice cautiously replied: "but I know I have to beat time when I learn music."

"Ah, that accounts for it," said the Hatter. "He won't stand beating. Now, if you only kept on good terms with him, he'd do almost anything you liked with the clock."

"Like make it run backwards?" interjected Alice.

"Of course," said the Hatter. "But we quarrelled last March and ever since then, he won't do a thing I ask. It's always six o'clock now! It's always tea time!"

A bright idea came into Alice's head. "Is that the reason there is so much food laid out?" she asked.

"Yes, that's it," said the Hatter with a sigh: "It's always tea time and we've no time to wash the things between whiles."

"Then you keep moving round, I suppose?" said Alice.

"Exactly so," said the Hatter: "as the things get used up."

"But what happens when you come to the beginning again?

"I want a clean plate," interrupted the Hatter: "Let's all move one place on."

He moved on as he spoke, and the Dormouse followed him: the March Hare moved into the Dormouse's place, and Alice rather unwillingly took the place of the March Hare. The Hatter was the only one who got any advantage from the change: and Alice was a good deal worse off than before, as the March Hare had just upset the chicken korma.

This piece of rudeness was more than Alice could bear: she got up in disgust and walked off; the Dormouse fell asleep instantly, and neither of the others took the least notice of her going, though she looked back once or twice, half hoping that they would call after her.

The last time she saw them, they were trying to put the Dormouse into a carrier bag, and the Dormouse was shrieking "Unexpected item in the bagging area!"

"At any rate, I'll never go there again," said Alice as she walked along the river past the London Central Mosque, which was shrouded in trees. "It's the stupidest tea-party I ever was at in my life!"

She walked on and was very soon in the beautiful gardens of Regents Park, among the bright flower-beds and the cool fountains.

## Chapter VIII

# The Queen's Croquet Ground
# at London Zoo

A large rose-tree stood before her: the roses growing on it were white but there were three gardeners at it, busily painting them with red crosses like flags of St George. Alice thought this a very curious thing, and she went nearer to watch them, and just as she came up to them she heard one of them say, "Look out now, Five! Don't go splashing paint over me like that!"

"I couldn't help it," said Five in a sulky tone; "Seven jogged my elbow."

On which Seven looked up and said, "That's right, Five. Always lay the blame on others!"

"*You'd* better not talk!" said Five. "I heard the Queen say only yesterday you deserved to be beheaded!"

"What for?" said the one who had spoken first.

"That's none of *your* business, Two!" said Seven.

"Yes, it is his business!" said Five, "and I'll tell him – it was for bringing the cook tulip-roots instead of mushrooms."

Seven flung down his brush, and had just begun "Well, of all the unjust things –" when his eye chanced to fall upon Alice, as she stood watching them, and he checked himself suddenly: the others looked around also, and all of them bowed low.

"Would you tell me," said Alice, a little timidly, "why you are painting those roses?"

Five and Seven said nothing, but looked at Two. Two began in a low voice, "Why the fact is, you see, Miss, this here ought to have been a St George's rose tree, and we put a white one in by mistake; and if the Queen was to find out, we should all have our heads cut off, you know. So you see, Miss, we're doing our best, afore she comes, to-" At this moment, Five, who had been anxiously looking across the garden, called out "The Queen! The Queen!" and the three gardeners instantly threw themselves flat upon their faces. There was a sound of many footsteps, and Alice looked round, eager to see who was coming. Having been to Buckingham Palace already, she wondered whether the opportunity to see the Queen twice on the same day might be rather excessive. And she had a niggling feeling that she may well be recognised from previous CCTV footage of her rather indiscreet change of size in the palace.

However, her fears were allayed when she spotted the Queen, who was a short plump personage and quite different from the dignified monarch of the United Kingdom and fifteen other Commonwealth realms, dressed in a gown and cap emblazoned with mother-of-pearl buttons.

Alice knew a little about the Pearly tradition, which had originated in the nineteenth century and was as much to do with raising money for London charities as it was about its street-trader background. She knew that its costumes were ornately and elaborately adorned with pearl buttons, often sewn into the shapes of symbols.

This Pearly Queen was accompanied by a Pearly King, and an entourage that were no more three-dimensional than the flat square gardeners.

They were followed by their guests, who were mostly other Pearly Kings and Queens, who really did look quite spectacular with their buttons shining and shimmering as the sun caught them. Among them Alice recognised the White Rabbit: it was talking in a hurried nervous manner, smiling at everything that was said, and went by without noticing her.

Alice was rather doubtful whether she ought not to lie down on her face like the three gardeners, as she was not familiar with the etiquette for meeting Pearly royalty, "but what would be the point of a procession," thought she, "if people had to lie down on their faces, so that they couldn't see it?" So she stood still where she was, and waited.

"Can you play croquet?" shouted the Pearly Queen, in a brisk cockney accent. "Yes!" shouted Alice.

"Come on then!" roared the Pearly Queen, "It's all for charity, you know!"

Alice followed the small procession, wondering very much what would happen next.

"It's – it's a very fine day!" said a timid voice at her side. She was walking by the White Rabbit who was peeping anxiously into her face.

"Very," said Alice, "where are we going?"

"Hush! Hush!" said the Rabbit in a low hurried tone.

The procession led into London Zoo, where Alice managed to get through the turn-style on a group ticket.

"Go to your places!" shouted the Pearly Queen in a voice of thunder, and people began running about in all directions, tumbling up against each other. This caused the monkeys in a nearby enclosure to break into a riotous furore, with much screeching and jumping. A giant gorilla looked on with rather more dignity.

"Don't be alarmed," said the Duchess, taking Alice by the arm. "She isn't as fierce as you may think. It's all part of the show!"

Past the tigers and the bearded pigs, the Pearly Queen strode with confidence until she reached the Flamingo area, then ordered her entourage to begin gathering up the pink birds where they stood.

"She seems very fierce to me," said Alice.

"It's just a bit of good old Cockney entertainment to raise money for the less fortunate!" said the Duchess.

They moved into a clearing and proceeded to lay out the pitch.

Alice thought she had never seen such a curious croquet ground in her life; it was all ridges and furrows; the balls were live hedgehogs, and it soon became clear that the mallets were fashioned from the live flamingos. The gardeners had to double themselves up and stand on their hands and feet, to make the arches.

The chief difficulty Alice found at first was in managing her flamingo: she succeeded in getting its body tucked away, comfortably enough, under her arm, with its legs hanging down, but generally, just as she got its neck nicely straightened out, and was going to give the hedgehog a blow with its head, it *would* twist itself around and look up in her face, with such a puzzled expression that she could not help bursting out laughing: and when she had got its head down, and was going to begin again, it was very provoking to find that the hedgehog had unrolled itself, and was in the act of crawling away: besides all this, there was generally a ridge or furrow in the way wherever she wanted to send the hedgehog to, and, as the doubled-up gardeners were always getting up and walking off to other parts of the ground, Alice soon came to the conclusion that it was a very difficult game indeed.

The players all played at once without waiting for turns, quarrelling the whole time and fighting for the hedgehogs, and in a very short time the Pearly Queen was in a furious passion, and shouting 'Off with his head!' or 'Off with her head!'

Suddenly Alice became aware that a hat was being passed round from one player to another, and each was digging deeply into their pockets to make a donation.

"All for charity! All for charity!" she heard each say as they passed the hat on.

The hat itself was quite a spectacle: a large velvet affair, decorated with playing card symbols made out of mother of pearl buttons, and festooned with white feathers.

"That's the spirit!" said the Duchess looking on, "It's all about helping one another and those less well off, even if you have little yourself!"

"Oh dear," said Alice, suddenly very perplexed. "I don't think I have any money on me and I'm not sure I can get to an ATM!" She turned her pockets out hurriedly. "I don't even have a button!" she said without thinking, and then realised the irony of this remark. "I have a travel card, if that is any good?"

"A travel card indeed!" said the Duchess with disapproval.

Alice began to feel uneasy. To be sure she had not as yet had any dispute with the Pearly Queen, but she knew that this was about to change. "And then," thought she, "what would become of me? They're dreadfully fond of beheading people here, whether it is just Cockney banter or not!"

The Pearly Queen took a couple of steps backwards as she circulated the hat and was now indignantly trying to identify which one of the group had wittily jeered "Caution, vehicle reversing!"

Alice took this as an opportunity to look for some way of escape, and suddenly spotted a figure wearing a placard pacing the pavement outside the railings. The placard was advertising trips to London's landmarks. However, it was not this that caught her attention, but the handbills he was holding. If she was not very much mistaken, he was giving out invitations to the mysterious Masked Ball!

Alice managed to dodge the croquet game, and squeeze herself out through the railings and onto the street.

66

# Chapter IX

# The Mock Turtle's Story
# at Mornington Crescent

As she approached the figure, she found that it was a Gryphon, standing in the middle of Prince Albert Road.

She did not quite like the look of the creature, but on the whole she thought it would be quite as safe to stay with it as to continue after the savage Pearly Queen.

"London Bridge, Tooley Street, The Shard… the Mock Turtle will show you them all," it announced, and then spoke more directly to Alice, "Have you taken the tour?"

"No, I haven't," said Alice, "though I have probably seen half of

London today."

"Please yourself," said the Gryphon, arranging the Masked Ball invitations that he was holding meticulously into a neat pile before they slipped out of his hand and scattered all over the pavement. Alice bent to help it gather them up.

"What's a Mock Turtle?" said Alice.

"It's the thing Mock Turtle Soup is made from," said the Gryphon.

"I already have an invitation to the Masked Ball," she mused, as she handed a pile of invitations back to the Gryphon.

"Do you now," said the Gryphon.

"But I do not know its whereabouts."

"Then you are in luck!" said the Gryphon. It was now grasping all the invitations again and forming them carefully into the shape of a fan, before dropping them all again on the ground. "The Masked Ball lies at the end of the tour. It is the last stop," it said.

"Can't I go straight to the ball without going on the tour?" said Alice, wearily.

"Mornington Crescent!!!" shouted the Gryphon triumphantly, as if just winning a game which had no apparent rules.

"I'm sorry but I haven't a clue what you are talking about!" said Alice. "How do I buy a ticket?" The Gryphon seemed so absorbed in gathering up his papers that he failed to answer.

"Hello?" She said, bending down over the hunched creature. Seeing that she was not making any further progress, Alice gave up and began to walk away.

"Some salesman," she said under her breath, "I could have bought a ticket!" Though Alice then remembered her embarrassment at London Zoo by the fact that she did not have any money.

In no time, Alice found that she had arrived at another underground station and that it was indeed Mornington Crescent. "Maybe the Gryphon was being more helpful than I gave it credit," she mused.

Faced with a set of closed barriers, Alice suddenly remembered the travel card that she had in her pocket and swiped herself through.

"If I need to take the tour, I think I should get south of the river," she said, as she waited for one of the station's lifts. She was soon descending once again below ground.

The station platform seemed to Alice to be deserted, before she spotted a creature sitting sad and lonely on a bench a good way off.

As she drew closer she decided that it must be the Mock Turtle. Alice sat down next to it, and there was an expectant silence between them.

"Are you taking the tour?" said the Mock Turtle after a while.

"Yes, I suppose I am," said Alice.

"I expect you want to hear my history," said the Turtle.

"Is it part of the tour?" said Alice.

"Of course. The tour always includes history," said the Mock Turtle. "Once, I was a real turtle."

These words were followed by a very long silence. Alice was very nearly getting up and saying, "Thank you, Sir, for your interesting story," but she could not help thinking there must be more to come, so she sat still and said nothing.

"When we were little," the Mock Turtle went on at last, "we went to school in the sea. The master was an old Turtle – we used to call him a Tortoise… because he taught us! We had the best of educations – in fact, we went to school every day."

"I've been to school every day, too," said Alice; "you needn't be so proud as all that."

"With extras?" asked the Mock Turtle a little anxiously.

"Yes," said Alice, "we learned French and music."

"And washing?" said the Mock Turtle.

"Certainly not!" said Alice indignantly.

"Ah, then yours wasn't a really good school," said the Mock Turtle in a tone of great relief. "Now at ours they had at the end of the bill, "French, music, *and washing* – extra."

"You couldn't have wanted it much," said Alice, "living at the bottom of the sea."

"I couldn't afford to learn it." said the Mock Turtle with a sigh. "I only took the regular course."

"What was that?" enquired Alice.

"Reeling and writhing, of course, to begin with and then different branches of arithmetic: ambition, distraction, uglification and derision."

"I never heard of 'Uglification,' "Alice ventured to say. "What is it?"

"You never heard of uglifying!" It exclaimed, "You know what to beautify is, I suppose?"

"Yes," said Alice doubtfully: "it means – to – make – anything – prettier."

"Well then, if you don't know what to uglify is, you *must be* a simpleton." said the Mock Turtle.

"What else did you learn?" said Alice.

"Well, there was Mystery," the Mock Turtle replied, counting off the subjects on his flappers, "Mystery, ancient and modern, with Seaography, then Drawling. The Drawling-master was an old conger-eel that used to come once a week: *he* taught us Drawling, Stretching, and Fainting in Coils."

"What was *that* like?" said Alice.

"Well, I can't show it to you myself," the Mock Turtle said: "I'm too stiff."

"My school taught the national curriculum until it converted to an academy," said Alice proudly.

"Well that sounds like a load of nonsense," said the Mock Turtle.

"How many hours a day did you do lessons?" said Alice, in a hurry to change the subject.

"Ten hours the first day," said the Mock Turtle, "nine the next, and so on."

"What a curious plan," exclaimed Alice.

"That's the reason they're called lessons," the Mock Turtle remarked, "because they lessen from day to day."

This was quite a new idea to Alice, and she thought it over a little before she made her next remark. "Then the eleventh day must have been a holiday?"

"Of course it was," said the Mock Turtle.

"And how did you manage on the twelfth?" Alice went on eagerly. Her voice was suddenly drowned out by an approaching underground train, and the two got to their feet as the wind buffeted them before the train emerged from the tunnel mouth with an explosive roar.

"That's enough about lessons," said the Mock Turtle. They both climbed aboard the train and the doors closed behind them. The carriage was empty, but as the train proceeded south along the Northern Line (via Bank), more creatures got on, gathering around the Mock Turtle as if they were joining the tour.

# Chapter X
# The Parking Quadrille

The Mock Turtle turned to Alice and said:

"You may not have lived much under the sea,"

"I haven't," said Alice.

"But have you driven in London?"

Alice could not see what this had to do with anything, but she replied nonetheless: "No never."

"Then you probably have never danced the Parking Quadrille!"

"No indeed," said Alice. "What sort of a dance is it?"

"Why," said the Mock Turtle, "you first form into a line, rather like a traffic jam - that generally takes some time – then you advance twice, each with a partner - then you reverse as if you were parallel parking (looking over your left shoulder, of course), then you check your watch, check for road signs, check for CCTV cameras and then you move again, and that's all the first figure."

"It must be a very pretty dance, said Alice timidly.

"Would you like to see a little of it?" said the Mock Turtle.

"Very much indeed," said Alice.

"Come, let's try out the first figure!" said the Mock Turtle.

A number of animals in the carriage rose from their seats and formed a line along the carriage, before the Mock Turtle broke into a slow song. Over the clatter of the train, it was sometimes difficult to hear, but Alice thought that the words went something like this:

*"Will you drop me at the market" said the whiting to the snail.*
*"Yesterday was pay-day, and I want to hit the sale."*
*"I have to keep on driving," said the snail, full of dismay,*
*"'Cos I'll have such trouble stopping if there is no parking bay!"*

*Will you, won't you, will you, won't you, will you park today?*

*Will you, won't you, will you, won't you, pay and display?*

"Could you not just let me out here?" said the whiting, keen to go,
"Well no, this is a red route," said the snail, so full of woe.
"Then just around the corner," said the whiting, playing cool.
"Not with zigzags on the curb-side 'cos it's just outside a school."

"I could simply jump out quickly, if it is just all the same,"
"Well you've picked a rather awkward spot, being a bus lane."
"Well maybe in five metres, I'm sure there'll be no fine,"
"I'd just rather not risk it - it's a double yellow line."

"Then take me to the roundabout, I'm sure there you can stop,"
"Well, that 's in the congestion charge and I'll be for the chop!"
"Could you maybe change direction by making a U-turn?"
"Why no, this is a one-way street – oh will you never learn?"

"So you cannot drop me anywhere? There really is no place?"
"Well not in a restricted zone, unless I find a space."
"Then take me home," the whiting said, getting rather miffed.
"And think again before you go to offer me a lift!"

*Will you, won't you, will you, won't you just let me alight?*
*We must not feed the meter 'cos the warden's sure to bite!*

Euston – Angel – Old Street – Moorgate – the creatures danced and danced in front of Alice, every now and then treading on her toes when they passed too close, or when the tube train turned a bend and they lost balance. As passengers got on and off, they too became embroiled in the dance for a moment and were trapped in a line of creatures, who were either reversing, or advancing twice with a partner. At London Bridge they all got out.

"Thank you, it's a very interesting dance to watch," said Alice, feeling very glad that it was over at last.

There was a slight hiatus as the creatures gathered at the station's exit in Duke Street. Alice's attention wandered for a moment to a man selling the evening newspaper and calling out the headlines: *"Giant brings West End to standstill. Flood damage costs millions. Read all about it!"*

On hearing this, Alice suddenly felt very uncomfortable, and shuffled her way into the middle of the group, in the hope that she may not be recognised.

*"…World Exclusive! Gigantic arm spotted at palace window!"* She heard these words as the party began to trail towards Southwark Cathedral, in the wake of the Mock Turtle, who had now elevated an umbrella for ease of identification.

They descended the stairs from Borough High Street into the market area, which lay in the shadow of the railway line.

"Borough Market has long been synonymous with food. As far back as the Eleventh Century, London Bridge attracted traders selling grain, fish, vegetables and livestock," declared the Mock Turtle. The creatures cooed as they heard this.

"The market still feeds the local community and has grown to over 100 individual stalls. It's unique reputation within the area has recently been marked by a Blue Plaque, voted for by the people of Southwark, marking it's place as London's Oldest Fruit & Vegetable Market."

As the tour wended its way through the stalls beneath the market's distinctive green-painted ironwork roof, the smell of wild boar sausages hung on the air and Alice began to feel rather hungry. Passing a specialist cheese shop, the Mock Turtle led the party onto Southwark Street, where they were for the first time confronted by a huge sky-scraper that had the appearance of an icicle shooting up into the sky.

"The Shard," began the Mock Turtle, "is the tallest building in Western Europe, transforming London's skyline with its 72-storey vertical city of offices, restaurants, residential apartments, hotel, and the capital's highest viewing gallery. It was inaugurated on 5 July 2012."

Alice was over-awed by the building that dwarfed her and everything else, and she craned her neck to see up to the top.
"Is that all it does?" said a particularly cross Walrus, who had boarded the tour at Old Street, and had not entered into any conversation since then.

"It's a feat of imagination, standing over one thousand feet high," said the Mock Turtle, "So…." the party stood expectantly waiting for the end of his sentence. After a moment he broke his silence: "Yes, that is all it does."

The Walrus shrugged.

A Mother Goose, whose children - Delilah, Sandy, and Aphra - had strayed from the party, was busy calling them back to the group. The tour proceeded.

"Tooley Street!" continued the Mock Turtle. "George Orwell, the famous author, lived here as a tramp to gain a first-hand view of poverty. He stayed here in September and October 1930, writing notes which eventually formed the book 'Down and Out in Paris and London'." The group nodded to one another in appreciation of the fact.

"Apparently a map dating back to the mid-sixteenth century shows that there was a pillory here, set up for punishing fraudulent traders, with a cage next to it to keep drunk and disorderly people who were arrested too late in the day to be imprisoned." Alice shuddered at the thought of being imprisoned and very much hoped that the tour would soon lead her off the street to somewhere that she did not feel so exposed to those who may have caught a glimpse of the evening headlines.

"… and here, tourists can experience a recreation of the Blitz."

The party continued to shuffle along behind the Mock Turtle with his elevated umbrella and Alice hardly recognised herself as she caught sight of her own reflection in a shop window, accompanied by a strange array of birds and animals. What a strange day it had been.

The Mock Turtle shuffled to a halt at the mouth of a tunnel.

"Weston Street!" it announced, "one of the dreariest places in London. It became a road tunnel as London Bridge Station expanded but in the early nineteenth century, before the station was built, the famous poet John Keats lived here, whilst a medical student at Guy's Hospital."

The tour group whooped accordingly.

Alice was now not really listening as her attention had been drawn to a green balloon trailing a red ribbon on the ground, which instantly reminded her of her long search for the location of the Masked Ball. As she bent down to pick it up, it was caught by the wind and floated into the air out of her reach. She watched it float away into the golden evening sky, unable to grasp it and wishing that she was a little taller again. She suddenly became aware of a great many echoing voices talking within the tunnel, and decided to leave the tour and venture along it into the darkness.

As her eyes became accustomed to the gloom, she made out a large queue of figures standing on the pavement along the right hand side, and as she got nearer she could see that they were queuing at a doorway cut into the tunnel wall.

The figures were even more weird and wonderful than the tour party that Alice had just left in Tooley Street, but all had one thing in common: they were all wearing carnival masks. What made their appearances still more bizarre was that, though each of them was a strange animal, many wore a mask depicting quite a different creature, so a shrew might be wearing a mask in the shape of a head of a cat; a bear might be wearing a head of a dog; and so on.

She was so excited to have finally happened on the location of what she could only assume was the Masked Ball, she joined the end of the queue, taking her place in the tunnel behind a wallaby, who was wearing the head of a ram.

"Man is least himself when he talks in his own person. Give him a mask, and he will tell you the truth," it said, and then added in a whisper "Oscar Wilde."

"Alice; pleased to meet you," said Alice offering her hand.

"No, those wise words were by Oscar Wilde," whispered the Wallaby.

"Oh," said Alice, suddenly somewhat perplexed that she was not wearing a mask herself.

"Then perhaps I am least myself after all," she answered. "I have been saying quite the same thing all day."

As she said this, she spotted the Gryphon, who she had last seen in Regents Park and who was now miraculously in the tunnel at London Bridge ahead of her. It was walking up and down the line of creatures, checking invitations, and at intervals dropping them and bending down with deliberation to pick them up again.

"Are you in the correct line?" said the Gryphon as he arrived at the end of the queue to address Alice. Alice hesitated.

"Are you on the guest list, or do you have a ticket?"

"Er, I have a ticket," said Alice, fishing it out of her pocket and showing the crumpled piece of paper. "But I thought there was only one queue."

"There is," said the Gryphon, taking Alice by the hand. "Come, follow me."

With that he took off at a pace, and Alice struggled to keep up. The party guests watched as she was led up to the front of the queue.

She followed the Gryphon through the doorway and found herself in a large hall with an arched ceiling, which she assumed must be under the train tracks of London Bridge Station. The hall was full of guests, all wearing bizarre and elaborate costumes which reminded her of a Venetian ball, the Notting Hill Carnival, and the Lord Mayor's show: all rolled into one. There were masked guests in satin crinolines or embroidered medieval breaches and tunics, there were guests in uniforms of all ranks and professions, there were nuns and magicians, politicians and dancers. There were even pretty girls in hot-pants serving jam tarts on silver platters. The music was provided by a small group of players whose stringed instruments were fashioned from live creatures, who patiently sat on their laps or at their feet, while the players strummed or bowed them.

Suddenly, Alice caught sight of the White Rabbit, dressed in a tuxedo, with a black mask covering his eyes, and decided to follow it. The rabbit led her further into what was a much larger chamber under the arches, with a stage at one end.

Without warning, there was a fanfare of trumpets, the lights were lowered, and the voices of the party guests shrank to a hush. The stage was suddenly lit in white light and everyone stood watching expectantly.

A procession began from the right of the stage: firstly ten soldiers carrying clubs. These were all shaped like the three gardeners that Alice had seen earlier at London Zoo, oblong and flat, with their hands and feet at the corners.

Next came ten courtiers, who were ornamented all over with diamonds and walked two-by-two as the soldiers did.

Then followed the Pearly King and Queen, who were coincidently accompanied by the thunderous roar of a train passing overhead.

Suddenly a cry of 'Trial's beginning!' was heard from the wings. As Alice craned her neck to try to see over the heads of the guests in front of her, she saw the Pearly King and Queen, their buttons glinting in the stage lights, now seated on the stage on thrones. Near the Pearly King was the White Rabbit with a trumpet in one hand and a scroll of parchment in the other.

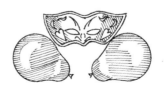

## Chapter XI

# The Trial Begins

"What trial is it?" Alice whispered to a bear standing next to her, who was wearing the mask of a dormouse, but she got no response and the mask just stared back at her with an unnervingly blank expression.

The judge was the Pearly King and the twelve jurors were creatures and birds. "Silence in court!" cried the White Rabbit, and the Pearly King put on his spectacles and looked anxiously round, to make out who was talking.

"Herald, read the accusation!" said the Pearly King, in a rough Cockney accent. On this, the White Rabbit blew three blasts on the trumpet, and then unrolled the parchment scroll, and read as follows:

*"There was a young lady called Alice,*
*who worried she was full of malice,*
*she cried lots of tears,*
*filled Whitehall with fears,*
*and she washed up at Buckingham Palace."*

Alice did not like the way this was going at all. The room was becoming quite restless now.

"Consider your verdict," said the King to the jury.

"Not yet, not yet!" The Rabbit hastily interrupted. "Call the first witness!"

The first witness was the Hatter. He came in with a tandoori chicken drumstick in one hand and a piece of naan bread in the other.

"Take off your hat!" said the Pearly King to the Hatter.

"It isn't mine," said the Hatter.

"Stolen!" the Pearly King exclaimed, turning to the jury.

"I keep them to sell," the Hatter added as an explanation, "I've none of my own. I'm a hatter."

Just at this moment Alice felt a very curious sensation, which puzzled her a good deal until she made out what it was: she was beginning to grow larger again, and she thought at first she would leave the ball, but on second thoughts she decided to remain where she was as long as there was room for her.

"I wish you wouldn't squeeze so," said the Dormouse-Bear (Alice could not really decide what it was). "I can hardly breathe."

"I can't help it," said Alice very meekly: "I'm growing."

"You've no right to grow here," said the Dormouse-Bear.

"Don't talk nonsense," said Alice more boldly, "you know you're growing too."

"Yes, but I grow at a reasonable pace," said the Dormouse-Bear. "Not in that ridiculous fashion." And he got up very sulkily and crossed over to the other side of the arched cavern.

All this time the Pearly Queen had never left off staring at the Hatter and, just as the Dormouse-Bear crossed the court, she demanded "Bring me a list of generous benefactors!" on which the wretched Hatter trembled so, that he shook both his shoes off.

"Give your evidence," the Pearly King repeated angrily, "or I'll have you executed, whether you're nervous or not."

"I'm a poor man, your Majesty," the Hatter began, in a trembling voice, "– and I hadn't begun my dinner – not above a week or so – and what with the naan bread and pickle getting so thin – and the twinkling of the tea –"

"The twinkling of the *what*?" said the Pearly King.

"It *began* with the tea, the Hatter replied.

"Of course twinkling begins with a T!" said the Pearly King sharply. "Do you take me for a dunce? Go on!"

"I'm a poor man," the Hatter went on, "and most things twinkled after that. My laptop died, you know."

"Oh, I *am* sorry," said the Pearly King.

"Get on with it!" shouted the Pearly Queen.

"– And the March Hare said..."

"I didn't!" the March Hare interrupted in a great hurry.

"You did!" said the Hatter.

"I deny it!" said the March Hare.

"He denies it," said the Pearly King: "Leave out that part."

"Well, at any rate, the Dormouse said –" the Hatter went on, looking anxiously round to see if he would deny it too, but there was silence. Alice was most confused to know if the Dormouse had now turned into a Bear, or vice-versa.

"After that," continued the Hatter, "I helped myself to some more chicken korma."

"But what did the Dormouse say?" one of the jury asked.

"That I can't remember," said the Hatter.

"You *must* remember," remarked the Pearly King, "or I'll have you executed."

The miserable Hatter dropped his chicken drumstick and his naan, and went down on one knee. "I'm a poor man, your Majesty," he began.

"You're a poor *speaker*," said the Pearly King. "If that's all you know about it, you may stand down," continued the Pearly King.

"I can't go any lower," said the Hatter: "I'm on the floor as it is."

"Then you may *sit* down," the Pearly King replied.

"I'd rather finish my dinner," said the Hatter, with an anxious look at the Pearly Queen, who was reading the list of benefactors.

"You may go," said the Pearly King, and the Hatter hurriedly left the court, without even waiting to put his shoes on.

"Why, they are only a pack of cards after all. I needn't be afraid of them!" she muttered. Unfortunately for Alice, in the hush her voice was easily heard and the Pearly Queen turned in her direction and pointed.

"Who is this?" she bawled. "Is she on the list of generous benefactors?"

Alice could feel her cheeks reddening as the throng of masked guests turned to look at her.

"My name is Alice, so please your Majesty," she said very politely.

"Where are you from?" cried the Pearly Queen.

"Hendon," said Alice.

"There was a young lady from Hendon…"

The White Rabbit began and then came to a pause. "Oh, could you not be from Westminster? Westminster works quite a deal better for the record:

"*There was a young girl from Westminster,*
*Who feared she would end up a spinster…*"

"Cockfosters!" shouted a guest.

"Walthamstow Central!" cried another.

"Mornington Crescent!" called the Gryphon from somewhere near the back.

## Chapter XII

# Alice's Evidence

"What do you know about this business?" the Pearly King said to Alice.

"Nothing," said Alice.

"Nothing *whatever*?" persisted the King.

"Nothing whatever," said Alice. This lie may have been plausible, if it had not been for the fact that Alice was growing at speed, and was now looking down over the throng of people that were looking back up at her.

"You are more than a mile high!" said the Pearly King.

"Nearly two miles high!" added the Pearly Queen.

"Let the jury consider the verdict," said the Pearly King.

"No, no," said the Pearly Queen. "Sentence first, verdict afterwards."

"Stuff and nonsense!" said Alice loudly. "The idea of having the sentence first!"

"Hold your tongue!" The Pearly Queen turned crimson with fury, and, after skimming through the names on her report once again, glared at her for a moment like a wild beast, screaming "Alice appears neither on the benefactors list, nor on the generous benefactors list. And I do recall that this is the very same person – though admittedly now much bigger – who played charity croquet, and then slid off without paying. Off with her head!"

"I am actually quite a generous little girl," Alice stammered.

"Well, you are certainly not little and I have seen no evidence of any generosity," said the Pearly King.

Alice could see no reason to stay another moment and began to make her move, knocking a number of creatures asunder as she squeezed herself through several arched doorways until she reached the exit onto the covered street outside.

The road tunnel was now deserted, but as she looked along it to her right, she spotted the silhouette of a policeman, who, on

seeing her size, instantly blew his whistle and pointed at her. Alice
took flight in the other direction, crawling and stumbling along
the tunnel until she was out again on Tooley Street. The Shard
somehow did not seem to her so high as she straightened up to
her full size.

She could see into the upstairs windows of buildings and spotted
her own image on a television in somebody's kitchen.

She was now being followed by an angry throng which seemed to
be steadily increasing in number. Cars were swerving and hooting
at her as she ran half along the road and half along the pavement,

followed by a bizarre stream of characters – creatures wearing masks, policemen blowing whistles.

"She's heading for the river!" She heard somebody yell, as she hastily turned a corner to try to dodge her pursuers.

She ran and ran along the water's edge and found, due to her height, that she could see easily over the roof of The Globe Theatre to where a Shakespearean play was being performed in the open air. As she reached Tate Modern, she changed direction and climbed up over the railing of the Millennium Bridge and began to cross it. By the time she had reached the middle, the bridge was swaying like a hammock, and several of her pursuers were thrown into the water, where they were swept away. She made it to the other side and mounted the steps – ten at a time – with an imposing view of St Paul's Cathedral ahead of her.

She was soon embroiled in a series of narrow streets full of banks and financial trading offices in the 'square mile' of the City of London, having left her pursuers far behind. She paused to catch her breath. It was silent all around her, but for the sound of some distant police sirens.

As she came to the imposing façade of the Royal Exchange, she spotted a homeless man sitting on the steps.

"Are you doing research for a novel?" Alice asked, remembering George Orwell's time living as a tramp. The man looked up at her with surprise. His clothes were ragged and dirty and he stored all that he owned in a single black refuse sack.

"No," he said. "I'm homeless. But thank you for noticing me. Most people just walk past and pretend I'm not here."

"Why would they do that?" said Alice.

"Because my presence makes people feel uncomfortable."

"There must be a lot of money around here," said Alice, looking around at the banks that were crammed together in London's financial quarter, the grandest of which was the Bank of England to her left.

"That's the irony of the thing," said the tramp. "Well, my aunt says that homelessness is a lifestyle choice, and that anyone homeless should get a job," said Alice.

"Believe me, I did not choose to live like this, sleeping on steps in the cold wind, and begging for money off strangers. Most of all, I wish I was not so hungry all the time."

"Well, you seem *very* nice to me," said Alice, pleased to be having a conversation with someone who was neither alluding to her monumental proportions, nor threatening to cut off her head. Suddenly she remembered the vegetable samosa that she had put in her pocket earlier. She fished it out and gave it to the man. For some strange reason, the samosa had increased in size at the same rate as herself and the homeless man could hardly embrace its huge dimensions with both arms.

"Thank you!" he said, overjoyed. "You are very kind. A true act of charity."

"It's all about helping one another and those less well off, even if you have little yourself!" said Alice, echoing the words of the Duchess that she had heard during the strange croquet game.

As it happened, Alice was beginning to feel very hungry indeed, but had seen that the man's need was greater than her own. She wondered whether it was possible to feel more hungry than usual, considering there was now more of her. However, this suddenly was not her primary concern, as she spotted her pursuers, who were running towards her along Queen Victoria Street, and had almost reached Bank Station. She needed to make a fast get-away and, taking flight, headed East.

She was getting quite out of breath again as she continued to run, but the crowd behind her was swelling and there was no opportunity to lose them.

"She's heading for the Tower of London! Off with her head!" she heard someone shout, as she passed the Port of London Authority Building and Trinity Square.

She ran faster and faster, passing the Tower complex. The Yeoman Warders stood watching her with their axes poised.

"Off with her head!" she heard the Pearly Queen's roar behind her.

Ahead of her now was Tower Bridge, beautifully lit in the twilight. Her size hindered her progress as she started to cross it, and she found she had to duck her head dramatically as she passed under the first tower. As she neared the middle, she heard a siren and wondered what it was.

"The bridge is going to open!" she heard someone shout from behind her.

Indeed she now became aware that the bridge was empty of traffic and she could see a tall ship on the River Thames beneath her, waiting to pass under the bridge.

She ran faster towards the middle as the road began to rise. Running up hill slowed her speed considerably but she struggled as fast as her legs could carry her. As she reached the mid point, the road split in two and she desperately launched herself across the widening gap, and made a leap for the other side.

"She's getting away!" she could hear the crowd still shouting behind her. She slid down the other side of the up-turned road and landed back on the South Bank again, panting hard.

She watched as several of her pursuers were jumping into the water, trying to span the river after her, but many of them were the flat soldiers that had formed part of the procession and they simply floated along with the current and out of sight.

"Who cares for you?" Alice shouted. She had grown to an

astronomic size by now. "You're nothing but a pack of cards!" At this the whole pack rose into the air and came flying down upon her.

She found herself lying on the bank of the Serpentine, with her head in the lap of her sister, who was gently brushing away some dead leaves that had fluttered down from the trees upon her face.

"Wake up, Alice dear!" said her sister. "Why, what a long sleep you have had!"

"Oh, I've had such a curious dream!" said Alice and she told her sister, as well as she could remember them, all the strange Adventures she'd had.

Alice got up and ran off, leaving her sister where she sat, leaning her head on her hand and watching the setting sun.

Alice was full of excitement, as she ran along the edge of the Serpentine, in the direction of the Royal Albert Hall. She loved London so very much, especially in the summertime, when the days were long and the concert-goers queued in Kensington for tickets to the Promenade concerts, and people stayed out late to enjoy the views and take the air. She loved London for all its strange characters and curiosities. She loved its history and its vibrancy and its diversity, and most of all she loved the fact that she could sample just about any cuisine from any corner of the world, right on her own doorstep. Although she had not seen so very many places yet, Alice had to declare that, in her opinion, London was the best city in the world.

THE END